D1252512

TALES OF THE GINSENG

The Mountain Spirit, an ink drawing from a fourteenth-century album, "Nine Songs," after Chao Meng-fu. The god is riding a leopard past an ancient pine and holds in his left hand the *ling chih,* the "marvelous herb" or "divine mushroom of immortality." *The Metropolitan Museum of Art, Fletcher Fund, 1973*

TALES OF THE GINSENG

edited and annotated by
Andrew C. Kimmens

William Morrow and Company, Inc., New York 1975

Grateful acknowledgment is made for permission to reprint the following:

"Treasure Hunt," Copyright 1954 by Samuel Hopkins Adams. Reprinted from GRANDFATHER STORIES, by Samuel Hopkins Adams, by permission of Random House, Inc. Originally appeared in *The New Yorker*.

"Der Berggeist" from DIE GINSENGWURZEL by André Eckhardt, by permission of Erich Roth Verlag, 1955.

Selections from the Lyman C. Draper Collection of the State Historical Society of Wisconsin: Draper's interview with Colonel and Mrs. Nathan Boone, and Daniel Boone's letter on the "Downfall of ginsagn."

Grateful acknowledgment is made for permission to quote from the following:

From STUDIES IN FRONTIER HISTORY: Collected Papers 1928-1958 by Owen Lattimore. Published by Oxford University Press. Reprinted by permission of the publisher.

From DERSU THE TRAPPER by V. K. Arseniev, translated from the Russian by Malcolm Burr. Copyright, 1941, renewed 1968, by E. P. Dutton & Co., Inc., and used with their permission.

From DERSU THE TRAPPER by V. K. Arseniev, translated from the Russian by Malcolm Burr, used with the permission of Martin Secker & Warburg Limited.

Printed in the United States of America.

1 2 3 4 5 79 78 77 76 75

Library of Congress Cataloging in Publication Data

Main entry under title:

Tales of the ginseng.

Bibliography: p.
Includes index.
1. Ginseng (in religion, folklore, etc.) 2. Tales, Oriental.
I. Kimmens, Andrew C.
GR790.G5T35 398.2'42 75-9888
ISBN 0-688-02942-6

Book design: Helen Roberts

For my parents

Preface

Throughout its long and honorable history in East and West, the ginseng root—*Panax ginseng* in the Orient, *Panax quinquefolium* in North America—has never ceased to fascinate those people who have known it. It was the most important drug possessed by the Chinese for two millennia: the essence of the perfect *yin,* the spirit of the soil, a potent restorative and tonic. Their neighbors, from whom the Chinese bought ginseng, the Tartars (Manchurians) and the Koreans, believed the root could work magic in men and that it was itself magic; ginseng in these countries was the object of a veneration just short of worship. Its discovery in the Americas was a capitalist's dream, producing trade and influence in the markets of China, and even a few American legends, which mainly tended to show that ginseng could make you rich. Ginseng has comparatively recently become available in health-food stores and naturopathic chemists all over the world.

But its place in cultural history is far from generally known. This book attempts to describe that place by assembling and organizing the stories, legends, beliefs, and discoveries that have revolved for years, disconnected and heterogeneous, around our perception of ginseng: here is the account of its history and use, the basis of its power and mystery.

There is no close case to argue in this book: no need to urge the greater popular or medical use of ginseng, or to press for more scientific research in the West on its therapeutic properties. Its use as a tonic and remedy is too well attested both in ancient times and now; its biochemical components are well enough understood by those who study them. The real importance of ginseng lies in its power to move men, to create legends, to excite veneration. This has not been documented before, and it has been my purpose here.

I want to acknowledge with thanks some help received. First I am grateful for the advice of Professor Owen Lattimore, the great anthropologist and Orientalist, and for the help on Manchurian and Mongolian lore provided by Dr. Caroline Humphrey of the Scott Polar Research Institute at Cambridge University. To Professor John A. Robertson of the University of Wisconsin I am indebted for his help with the Boone material. Mrs. Dorothy Macdonald prepared the index with great skill. Mr. Kuang-fu Chu of the Oriental Division, New York Public Library, kindly drew the Chinese characters in the Korean tales. Dr. Charles Curwen of London University's School of Oriental and African Studies provided excellent translations from Chinese of the wonderful Kirin tales. Other translations are my own, along with all responsibility for whatever is incomplete, inaccurate, or inadequate in this book. Discovering what people have thought and believed on any subject of importance in cultural history has always been the hardest study of all.

New York City
September, 1974

Contents

List of Illustrations

TALES OF THE GINSENG

Power of the Ginseng: Folk Tales

The following stories attest to the great power of the ginseng root among the people who live where it grows and is sought for. Although ginseng has been cultivated in Korea and Japan for centuries, the roots grown by men do not have the power innate in wild roots. Miraculous cures come by legend only from wild roots, the tutelary divinities will have to do only with wild roots, and the fabulous prices—fifteen hundred dollars an ounce or more—one now hears of ginseng fetching can only be related to wild roots from the former imperial preserve in southwestern Manchuria.

These are folk tales, essentially: stories coming from the people, in which nearly everyone is poor—those who are not usually do some evil and get punished. Ginseng as medicine, at least since the beginning of the Manchu Imperial monopoly in the seventeenth century, was inaccessible to the vast majority of the people. But this would probably have increased its importance among the people as a source of stories and legends: the wondrous aspects of any stories that may already have existed would only have become accentuated by scarcity.

In the Kirin stories—they are named after the province in southern Manchuria where the most valuable wild ginseng grows—the ginseng root can transform itself into quasi-human beings, often with magical powers, who are particularly vulnerable to ill-intentioned hunters, but whose strength derives from the soil and is ultimately invincible. The tales from

Korea introduce a divinity, the spirit of the mountains and rivers, creator and protector of the ginseng, who uses the root to accomplish feats of good will toward men and to resolve conflicts among them.

The original versions of these tales, now translated into English for the first time, were written down earlier in this century. The tales themselves are certainly much older, though as with all folklore it is not possible to say just when they first came to be told, or even when they first attained their present form.

THE ORIGIN OF GINSENG: THE STORY OF ULA-JAN *

At an ancient time, in the reign of the Emperor Yan-di, nearly three thousand years ago, in one of the great cities in the valley of the Ussuri, lived a rich and pious man called Ula-jan, a man loving, good, and wise. His joy was to do good for the poor and to cure the sick. Therefore the god Fo (Buddha) became his friend, protecting him and crowning all his undertakings with success. Ula-jan saw his prosperity grow from day to day, and soon his riches surpassed even the treasures of the Son of Heaven, the wise Emperor Yan-di.

Ula-jan was nearly a hundred years old, but in spite of this great age he remained as strong and healthy as a man of forty. In this same city lived Jang-loon, also a rich man, but evil, cruel, and proud. He never helped the poor but loved to take from them what little they had. This envious man took offense at the prosperity of Ula-jan, whose great riches kept Jang-loon from all spiritual repose, kept him awake at night, and made him lose his appetite. Night and day he tried to think of a way to take away Ula-jan's goods and to destroy the good man's happiness. After thinking about it for a long time, he

* Michel Delines (pseud. of Mikhail Osipovich Ashkinazi), "A la recherche du genn-chenn, d'après les explorations de M. Maximov," *Bibliothèque Universelle et Revue Suisse,* vol. 37, Lausanne, 1905, pp. 329–332.

came upon his plan of crime. He made wounds on his legs, covered himself with rags, took up crutches, and went as a poor mendicant to beg at the *fansa* * of Ula-jan.

The good man, suspecting nothing, greeted the false beggar with kindness, dressed him, gave him shelter, food, and money, and cured his wounds. Jang-loon, even while accepting the kindnesses of his enemy, observed how his home was set out, so as to discover the hiding-place of his treasures. That night he plunged a knife into the heart of Ula-jan, who immediately expired, uttering no cry, as if he were waiting for death and was not surprised by the attack.

Jang-loon began at once to rifle through the cabinets of his victim. He opened the first, plunged in his bloody hand, but snatched it back with horror: the chest was full of vipers. In the second cabinet, instead of silver he found a monstrous beast. Overcome with horror, the murderer was running from the house, when all at once the *fansa* was lit with a blinding flash of light, and before the terrified eyes of the guilty man appeared the god Fo. The criminal, trembling from head to toe, fell on his face.

"Cruel and ungrateful Jang-loon!" roared Fo. "You have committed the greatest of crimes. You have killed the man who sheltered you, who cured your wounds, who dressed and nourished you. You would have stolen his treasures, but I changed them into serpents and horrible beasts, because the riches of Ula-jan were, and are still, in himself. Take up the corpse of this holy man, carry it on your shoulders into the mountains of Sikhote-Alin, and bury the precious remains under a hidden rock. As for myself, I will take care that the memory of the magnanimous Ula-jan lives as long as the world lasts. And in all that time men shall never forget your hateful crime. When you have buried Ula-jan, you will die, crumbled to a thousand pieces, and each piece of your body will change into a red wolf, so that all may see on you the blood of the man you have killed. And you will remain for thousands

* Small house in the country.

upon thousands of years the guardian of the treasures into which I shall change the relics of Ula-jan. Go immediately and execute my will!"

The god disappeared. Jang-loon, made speechless by this overpowering force, took upon his shoulders the body of Ula-jan and began to walk toward the mountains, as he was told. For many months, day and night, he walked without growing tired, and finally reached the range of Sikhote-Alin. Then Fo's benevolent power was manifest. Suddenly Ula-jan's mortal wound opened, and perfumed blood flowed out, drop by drop, from his miraculously preserved body. Each drop of blood penetrated deep into the earth, and from each spot there immediately sprang up the wondrous ginseng plant.

The murderer wandered for a long time in the mountains, his victim on his shoulders, searching for a deep and hidden valley; the blood of Ula-jan continued to flow, and ginseng bloomed everywhere it fell. Several times Jang-loon halted and placed the body on the ground. Immediately there grew up all around the herb *ula-zao,* Fo's second gift to the poor in memory of the holy Ula-jan. *Ula-zao* is a kind of rush, so soft and pithy that many Chinese, in winter, put it inside their shoes to serve as stockings.

Finally Jang-loon discovered the deep and empty valley, inaccessible to mere mortals, and there buried the body of Ula-jan. As soon as he threw the last clod of earth on the body of his victim he crumbled into a thousand pieces, which became a thousand red wolves. The valley changed by magic into a wondrous garden filled with plants of the miraculous ginseng. The rats and mice that came into this valley were changed into precious sables, and this was Fo's third gift in memory of holy Ula-jan, for until then the sable was unknown.

By Fo's will, the wolves will last only so long as there is one ginseng plant still not uprooted. There are a thousand wolves, neither more nor less; they neither reproduce nor die. They devour all the unfaithful Sons of Heaven * who dare to

* This is a periphrasis for "Chinese," but *cf.* p. 108n.

steal the most precious Gift of Heaven, the ginseng root. Only the poor Chinese can profit from the virtues of this miraculous root which cures all ills, as the great Ula-jan did himself.

THE GINSENG SPIRIT: KIRIN TALES

THE GINSENG SPIRITS*

Some say that in former times, before it took refuge deep in the mountains east of the pass (i.e., in Manchuria), ginseng used to grow in the great plain of Hopei. The turnips that grow there nowadays were left behind by the ginseng when it went away.

In those early days there was a rich man who lived in a village on the great plain. Before he retired to the countryside he had been an official in the capital and everyone called him Secretary Hu. He employed a servant-boy only fifteen years old, who had to do all the work. When he got up early in the morning the boy had to carry water from the well, then sweep the courtyard, feed the draft animals and the pigs, mill flour, chop wood, and clear out the dung. He never had a spare moment, and if he was slow he could expect a scolding, if not a beating. Secretary Hu made him work like an ox and fed him like a dog, so the boy was always in tears.

One day, when the heavens were still full of stars, the boy went as usual to the outskirts of the village to fetch water. When he came in sight of the well he noticed what appeared to be two spots of red darting about around the well. When he got closer he saw that they were two children, five or six years old, exactly alike. They were fair skinned and plump,

* The tales in this section are excerpted from a collection of traditional tales: Chih feng, *Chi-lin min-chien ku-shih* (Folk tales of Kirin), Shanghai, 1961. The translation is by Charles Curwen.

had long black hair, bare bottoms and bare feet, and wore red aprons. They were leaping about on their little feet all around the well in a very fetching manner. The boy was immediately taken with them and hurried over to question them.

"Whose family are you from? It's dangerous to play around here."

The children looked at him but said nothing.

"Are you lost?"

They shook their heads.

"Are you hungry?"

Again they shook their heads.

"Are you thirsty?"

Only then did the children nod slightly.

So the boy drew two buckets of water and the children buried their heads in the buckets and drank. Then they smiled at him, wiped their mouths and, running down the road toward the fields, soon vanished. From that time onward, each morning when the boy went to draw water, the children would come and drink and then run off without a word. The boy was very curious and became more and more attached to the children. If only they would say a few friendly words to him!

A hundred days passed. Then one day, after the children had drunk, they spoke for the first time.

"Little brother, we've settled down now. Why not come over to our home and play?"

The boy was very pleased. He could not resist the temptation, so he put down the buckets and followed the children. They went along the road, along paths and through the fields until they reached a wood, carpeted with long grass and filled with all kinds of wildflowers. In the green and shadowy wood the wind rustled, and it was beautifully cool and fragrant.

"What a lovely place you have!" said the boy with a sigh.

"Don't you have a good home, little brother?"

"Me? I have no home." And he told them all about the dog's life he led working for Secretary Hu.

"What a wolf of a man!" exclaimed the children. "But come with us." They took him behind a mound, where two green leafy plants were growing. The children pulled them up by the roots. They were yellowish white with a touch of red, and with a few fine whiskers—like turnips, only smaller.

"We've drunk your water for a hundred days, little brother, so we'll give you these two plants," said the children, putting them into his hand. "Exchange them with Secretary Hu for a three-room house and ten *mu* of land, so that you can set up a home for yourself."

The boy was delighted. In an instant the children rolled over on the ground and vanished.

When Secretary Hu got up that morning he could not find the boy anywhere, and cursed him from one end of the street to the other. When he saw the boy returning with empty water buckets he flew into a rage and rushed at him to give him a beating. But the boy ducked and said firmly:

"Not so much cursing and beating, Secretary Hu! I'm leaving you today, and I'm going to live on my own."

Secretary Hu realized that there was something behind this and began to question the boy who, holding the plants in his hand, explained everything to his master. Secretary Hu agreed to give him the house and the land, then took the two plants. They were ginseng of the highest quality! So those two children were ginseng spirits! These roots would cure sickness and prolong life! They were worth a lot of money too. If he could lay his hands on the ginseng spirits and present them to the Emperor he would be rewarded with a mountain of gold and silver! As these thoughts flashed through his mind he gobbled up the two ginseng roots, then said to the boy:

"I'll give you the house and the land, but not until you've found those two children so that I can see them."

"But the children have gone. I'll never find them."

Secretary Hu seized a whip and forced the boy to go with him and search. They searched in the wood but found no trace of the children; where the ginseng plants had been plucked up there was nothing but soft earth. The boy was secretly pleased, but Secretary Hu was very disappointed. Then he thought, "If the boy can see ginseng spirits, then he'll be able to find them. I'd better not try to force him . . ."

"Never mind," he said. "I'll give you the house and land anyway. Let's hurry back home and draw up a contract."

"With a house and land," thought the boy happily, "I won't have to put up with Secretary Hu's oppression any more." He would work hard on his land, get married, and life would be just fine.

When they reached home Secretary Hu called his accountant, a scribe, and a witness, and they drew up a contract, which Hu and the boy both signed. Only then did the witness read the contract to the boy: "The boy willingly agrees to pay two ginseng plants and two ginseng spirits in return for which Secretary Hu will give him a three-room house and ten *mu* of land. Neither party shall default."

When the boy heard this his eyes flashed with anger.

"What's this? Who said I would give you the ginseng spirits?"

"Who said so?" replied Secretary Hu with an icy smile, "You did. Here's the witness and here's the contract. Don't you dare to back down! And let me tell you, if you try to run away, there are officials everywhere and I've only to issue a warrant and you'll be seized and brought back. So clear off and find those ginseng spirits!" And he chased the boy out of the house.

With anger and hatred in his heart and indignation in his belly, the boy went into the wood, sat down near the mound and cried. He cried until nightfall, till the stars and the moon came out, till the dew rose. He cried and cried, then lay down beside the mound and fell asleep.

Suddenly, as he slept, someone shook him. He opened his eyes. It was just daylight, about the time when he usually went to draw water, and the two children were standing there, smiling at him.

"You've got your own home now, little brother. What are you doing sleeping here?"

"There's no hope for me. I've come for the last time, to say good-bye." He told them, through his tears, about the false contract and the warrant.

"That grasping and slippery Secretary Hu!" said the children angrily. "What a hateful man! We have been in many places, and we hoped to settle down here forever when we saw how rich the land is. Who would have guessed that there would be a man like Secretary Hu to spoil our plans. All right, little brother, take us to see him."

"No, no! He's sure to destroy you. I won't let you go to him. Let's play here a little together, then you go away. I would rather let him take me to court."

"No, little brother, you take us to him. We can save you and punish him at the same time. He wants to destroy us, but nothing could be more difficult." When he heard this the boy felt more at ease, so he led the children to Secretary Hu's house.

When he saw the two ginseng spirits Secretary Hu was beside himself with joy. The children made him renounce the false contract and agree to hand over the house and land. Then the boy sadly took leave of them, and the children asked:

"Secretary Hu, what are you going to do with us?"

"I'll give you to the Emperor and get a reward. I'll be a rich man."

"All right. Then prepare a big jar of water, and we'll take a bath. When we are clean we will come with you."

So Secretary Hu sent for a large jar full of clean water, which was placed in the courtyard. The children immediately jumped in and sank to the bottom, whereupon the water turned yellow. Shortly afterward they leaped out of the jar and floated about in the air, calling out to Secretary Hu:

"We are going away, Secretary Hu. But since you've taken so much trouble on our account we cannot let it go for nothing. Pour this water into the fields and you will harvest even more, even better ginseng. You'll make an even greater fortune when you present the crop to the Emperor." So saying, with a wave of their little arms and legs, they flew off beyond the pass.

When the ginseng spirits had gone Secretary Hu could only gape. There was nothing to do but pour the water from the jar onto the land as they had instructed. Strange to relate, as soon as the water had seeped into the soil, on the damp ground there immediately appeared a field of big and flourishing ginseng! When they were dug up there were red ones, yellow ones, and white ones—even thicker and juicier than ordinary ginseng. Secretary Hu tried some and found them even tastier than ginseng usually is.

He was transported with delight. Leaving some for replanting, he had the rest uprooted and loaded a cart full. He thought to himself, "This must be 'miraculous ginseng'—even better than ginseng spirits. The Emperor will be delighted." His servants drove the cart while he rode on horseback, and joyfully they took the "miraculous ginseng" to the capital.

When the Emperor saw that Secretary Hu had presented so much "miraculous ginseng," his pleasure knew no bounds. He praised Secretary Hu and then had him conducted to the Pleasure Pavilion to rest, so as to be ready to receive his reward. He ordered all the ginseng to be brought to the golden throne room; then he tried one. It was juicy, cool and sweet—really delicious. He had seen ginseng before and had eaten it, but he had never come across any so fine and tasty. The more he looked at them the better he liked them, the more he ate the better they tasted. He thought, "Ordinary ginseng gives long life, but this must give eternal youth. I'll eat my fill and never grow old. I'll live forever and will always be Emperor." He selected the biggest and gobbled it up, then went on eating until his belly was fat and round, until he could eat no more, and only then did he stop. Then he began to feel uncomfortable, and his belly began to rumble. He thought it might be better if he moved about a little, but as soon as he left his dragon throne—ugh! he threw up all over the ground and then was seized with diarrhea. The servants quickly carried him to the inner palace, where he collapsed moaning and groaning on his bed and went on spewing from both ends. Immediately the court physician was summoned. He made a few inquiries and then asked to see the "miraculous ginseng."

"Your Majesty," he concluded, "this is not 'miraculous ginseng.' These are turnips, which only look like ginseng."

When the Emperor heard this he was furious. He immediately signed an imperial warrant and sent it out. Secretary Hu was sitting in the Pleasure Pavilion hoping that the Emperor would hurry up and give him his reward. He was thinking to himself that the Emperor would be so pleased with the "miraculous ginseng" that he would not be content to give him a mountain of gold and silver, but would grant him half the Empire. At the thought he grinned with pleasure and his mouth watered so much that the saliva went three feet down his chest. Just at this moment he heard a cry from the Gold Palace: "The donor of ginseng to receive the Imperial Command!" He quickly ran out of the Pleasure Pavilion, knelt down, and made the three obeisances and nine kowtows. Then the Imperial Command was read out:

"Secretary Hu passed off turnips as ginseng in order to deceive the Emperor, giving rise to vomiting and diarrhea which has still not ceased. His offense is enormous. He is to be beheaded immediately!"

Secretary Hu was thunderstruck. Armed guards came and seized him and dragged him out through the palace gates. Before he had time to utter a word his head was off.

Since that time, in the great plain of Hopei, only turnips grow, and they look very much like ginseng.

THE GINSENG TREASURES

There once lived a boy called Ma-lin. His parents had died when he was very young, and he lived with his uncle. This uncle was a man who would do anything for money, and people called him "Ma the Grub." Ma-lin had only leftovers to eat and old tattered clothes to wear. He had to chop all the wood and carry all the water, not to mention the milling and husking. If he got on the wrong side of Ma the Grub he would be scolded or beaten.

Ma the Grub was a ginseng gatherer. One year, when he went as usual with a few men into the great mountains to search for ginseng, he took the twelve-year-old Ma-lin with him. They passed over several high mountains and crossed many peaks, and everyone was tired, yet they had not found a single ginseng plant. But Ma the Grub was an experienced ginseng hunter, and he pointed ahead to a woody hill and said, "There is ginseng there." The other men were a little doubtful, but they followed him nevertheless. Little Ma-lin was afraid that if he fell behind he would be lost in the deep mountains and would never see any other people. He might even be eaten by wild animals. So he did his best to keep up. But his feet were blistered, and he had to collect plants for the others to eat as well. His heart was as bitter as yellow lotus seeds, but no one would take any notice of his tears.

They arrived at a small mountain, which was joined to the imposing height of South Mountain, with its luxuriant cover of green forest and its craggy rocks like white jade. A small river below bubbled and rippled like a stream of silver. Ma the Grub stood on the slope and looked everywhere. "It would be strange," he said with a frown, "if there were no ginseng in a place like this." So when night fell they stopped there.

Early the next morning a bird suddenly began to sing. As soon as he heard it Ma the Grub jumped up, threw on his clothes, and went to look. When he came back he said to the others, "That's a ginseng bird, so there must be ginseng nearby." Everyone was pleased, and they pitched their tents. Ma the Grub told Ma-lin to guard the camp while he took the others to hunt for ginseng on the slopes of South Mountain on the other side of the stream.

Left alone at the camp, Ma-lin soon got bored. He started to wander around, looking at the scenery, when suddenly he saw, drinking at the stream below, a little girl, plump and naked except for a red apron, with twelve heaven-piercing pins in her hair. Her face was as rosy as an apple, and she seemed to be eleven or twelve years old. Ma-lin, who had never had anyone but his tyrannical uncle for company, was delighted to see a playmate of his own age, and stood on the cliff and called down to her:

"Little girl! Come up here and play! We'll hunt for treasure and ride wooden horses." The girl looked up and saw Ma-lin with his ragged clothes and broken shoes. But his thin face was lively, his eyes were clear, and she knew at once that he was a trustworthy lad. Nevertheless she turned away with a grimace and said, "No, you're up to no good. I'm not going to play with you." And she went on drinking from the stream.

"I don't mind if you don't play with me, but how can you say I'm up to no good?"

"How can I know you're not?"

"Come and play. I won't bully you, I won't quarrel with you, I won't lie to you, and I'll do everything you ask. How's that?" The girl stood up and wiped her hands on her apron.

"Do you mean it?"

"I've never lied in all my life." So the girl skipped happily up the slope, and the two of them went off hand-in-hand to play. The girl told Ma-lin stories about tigers and bears that lived in the mountains; Ma-lin told her about the hard life he led. He plucked flowers to put in her hair, and she picked fruit from the trees for him to eat. The more they talked the better they got on; the more they played the happier they became. At nightfall the girl said, "Your uncle will be back soon. I'll go now, but whatever you do don't tell anyone about us." They agreed to meet the next day, and the little girl went off.

Before long Ma the Grub and the others returned, and sure enough, they had found some ginseng. They were not very pleased with it, however, because Ma the Grub was sure that in these mountains there was "treasure" to be found. What they called "treasure" was ginseng of more than eight ounces in weight. So Ma the Grub spent every day from dawn to dusk hunting, but he did not find the "treasure" he was hoping for.

The little girl came to play with Ma-lin every day, and they became fast friends. When the others were not there they were inseparable. Ma-lin's complexion became clear and rosy, and he seemed full of life. Ma the Grub noticed the change, and one day he took Ma-lin to where the others could not hear and asked him where he had been going every day. Ma-lin was on the point of telling him when he suddenly remembered what the little girl had said.

"I've been playing by myself around the mountain," he said in a low voice.

"What can you be playing at, all by yourself?" Ma-lin could not think of an answer right away and blushed. Ma the Grub was pleased at this and said, "You're a good boy, Ma-lin. Come now. I'll find out even if you don't tell me. You'd better come clean if you don't want us to fall out!" Ma-lin thought that the cat was out of the bag, so he told his uncle all about the little girl. Ma the Grub was so pleased that he even embraced the boy. "You are my good little boy, my lucky charm." He brought him back to the camp, gave him good things to eat, and that night gave him a good thick quilt to cover himself with.

The next day, before he left, he gave Ma-lin a red ribbon. "When you are playing with the girl today tie this ribbon around the little braid on the top of her head, in the middle. If you do this it will be worth a real reward and when we get home you'll have good food and drink and comfort."

Ma-lin stood on the hillside, the red ribbon in his hand, waiting for the girl. Soon she came, but she was shocked to see the red ribbon in his hand and turned and ran, calling back, "I said you were up to no good and you wouldn't admit it. What is that red ribbon for? What have you got it for?"

"It's for your hair, that's all."

"You've been listening to someone evil. You want to destroy me. I won't play with you any more. Not any more!"

Ma-lin scratched his head in puzzlement. "What harm will it do to put a red ribbon in your hair?"

"The old ones told me that if I'm tied with a red ribbon I'll be recognized and that will be the end of me."

When he heard this, Ma-lin immediately tied the red ribbon to a stone and threw it into the stream. The girl saw that Ma-lin was true to her after all and came back to play with him.

That evening Ma-lin, in tears, was forced to tell Ma the Grub about how the girl had seen the red ribbon in his hand and had refused to play with him, and how he had thrown the ribbon into the stream. He got a beating on the spot. Then his uncle took another ribbon from his pocket and tied a slip-knot in it. "Tomorrow slip this on while she is not looking and bring her back here. Don't let her go and wait for me to come back. If you do this I'll make you rich and happy. I'll give you anything you want. If you don't catch her, you'll eat bitterness!" He took out his dagger and brandished it. "I'll cut off your feet and leave you in the mountains for the tigers and wolves!"

The next day, after Ma the Grub and the others had gone, the little girl came, and they climbed a tall tree together to pick some fruit. The leaves kept falling one after the other onto the girl's head. "Feel them all," she said, and Ma-lin took that opportunity to slip the red ribbon over the tuft of hair on the top of her head. By the time she realized what had happened it was already tightly knotted and Ma-lin grasped the end of the ribbon for fear she would escape.

"I said you were evil," she said with tears in her eyes, "but you denied it. Now look—you want to ruin me!"

"My uncle Ma wants to see you, that's all. What are you frightened of?"

"You don't understand. I'm a mountain ginseng girl. Your uncle wants to sell me. If I fall into his hands I am lost." And her tears fell like a string of pearls. "You humans—your hearts are blacker than mountain grapes. It's my fault for being blind and trusting you." Ma-lin, totally ignorant of all this, was surprised and distressed.

"Since you are a ginseng girl I will let you go." So he untied the ribbon and the girl vanished like a wisp of smoke.

When Ma the Grub heard that his nephew had caught the ginseng girl and then let her go, he beat him until he was more dead than alive and made him go in search of the girl once more. But the girl came no more. In a passion of fury Ma the Grub actually took out his dagger and cut off the boy's feet. Then he threw him into a ravine on South Mountain, together with the red ribbon.

"If you can catch the girl I'll have you carried back and your feet healed; if you don't you can stay here and feed the tigers and wolves."

Ma-lin became unconscious and did not come to until after nightfall. With an effort he raised his head: stars dotted the sky and blinked at him. Everywhere it was dark; the trees stood straight all around and a hanging cliff towered awesome above him. The pain in his legs was unbearable and he began to moan. After a long time he wiped his eyes and turning this way and that called out:

"Ginseng girl, I'm suffering for your sake, but I bear you no grudge. Surely you can come and keep me company?" Then the wind rose and the whole forest began to stir and wave about. Suddenly the boy saw, not far from him, a ginseng plant with twelve leaves, green and luxuriant, growing alone, far from other plants. Ma-lin slowly crawled over to it and took out the red ribbon, intending to tie up the ginseng. "This is surely a treasure," he said to himself. But as he got nearer the ginseng began to change, and change, and change—and there was his little friend again, the ginseng girl. She asked him what had happened and he told her everything.

"Ah!" she sighed. "All this is my fault. I'll tell you what: you must give me to them and then they will take you home."

"How could I do that? We must stay together." And they cried, cheek to cheek.

"I know!" exclaimed the girl. "Tie a knot that looks like a slipknot and put it over my hair, and tomorrow give me to Ma the Grub. Ask for your feet back, and while I'm running away, fix them back on." So the boy did as she said and attached the ribbon to her hair.

The next day Ma the Grub came to the ravine and when he saw that the treasure was captured he was delighted. He took up the girl in his arms and told his man to carry Ma-lin back to the camp. After they arrived he began to think about the value of his treasure.

"What is the price of ginseng treasure?" he asked Ma-lin. But how was the boy to know? He merely bowed his head.

When his uncle pressed his question Ma-lin stretched out and lay down. When he saw this Ma the Grub cried, "Your Honor speaks? The price is one *tang*." * Ma-Lin was so furious that he turned over. "Ah, the price is two *tang!*" Exasperated by this the boy turned over eight times in succession. So Ma the Grub fixed the price at ten *tang*.

"I don't want the money!" said the boy. "All I want is my feet back, then have me carried back to the ravine where I was." The uncle agreed.

After nightfall the ginseng girl waited until no one was watching, then stealthily untied the slipknot and ran back to the ravine. Ma-lin had already fainted several times because of the pain. The girl snipped off two of her own toes and as soon as she did this two tender white new ones grew in their place. Then she fixed Ma-lin's feet onto his ankles and put her own two toes into his mouth. They tasted sweet and fragrant, and he immediately felt full of vigor. When he looked at his feet they had already healed, so he could run and jump again. His legs were even lighter than they had been before.

When Ma the Grub found that the ginseng girl had run away he knew that he had been tricked. He looked for Ma-lin, but as soon as the boy saw him he took to his heels. Ma-lin ran ahead and Ma the Grub followed. Ma-lin ran very fast; he ran to the edge of the ravine, but it was too far for him to jump across and with one blow of his club Ma the Grub killed him.

The ginseng girl found Ma-lin's body and realized that he had suffered because of her, and she wept and wept. Then she bit her tongue, forced open the boy's jaw, and let some of her juice fall into his mouth, so that Ma-lin came alive again. But this time there were twelve heaven-piercing pins in his hair, his face was all white and red—in short, he had turned into a ginseng treasure.

Ma the Grub still would not give up; he stayed in the mountains hunting ginseng treasure. One day he suddenly

* *Tang* means "to lie down," but among ginseng hunters one *tang* means 480,000 *liang* (ounces) of silver.

caught sight of the ginseng girl and Ma-lin hand-in-hand, and in Ma-lin's hair there were twelve heaven-piercing pins. He realized that Ma-lin had turned into a ginseng treasure as well. He made up his mind to have these two treasures for himself, so he dismissed the others. When the girl and Ma-lin discovered that Ma the Grub had not left the mountain but still had evil designs on them, they took to their heels at once. Ma the Grub followed. Mountains could not hinder them, ravines could not stop them. Ma-lin and the girl crossed them as if they were walking on flat ground. Not so Ma the Grub: he could not keep up with them. But still he would not give up. Day after day he chased them, month after month, year after year. He chased and he chased until he died of exhaustion in the mountains. The pair of ginseng treasures, hand-in-hand, lived and played together and were never parted.

THE GINSENG WIFE

The Ch'ang-pai Mountains in the Northeast are famous for ginseng. One year a young man named Wang arrived from the province of Shantung. His family was very poor and had only a straw-thatched hut with three rooms to live in, and the roof leaked and let the rain in. What with drought one year after another and crop failures, the family just could not make ends meet. When Young Wang heard that it was possible to make a living gathering ginseng in the mountains east of the pass he made his way there, though with immense difficulty. The first year he had a companion to go with him gathering ginseng, a man introduced to him by someone from his own village. But they found little, only enough to provide them with food, and no big roots. The following year, when the season started, Young Wang took a two-stringed fiddle with him, which he played whenever he had time. As he was only a beginner at ginseng gathering and did not know the customs and rules, no one wanted to accompany him. So Young Wang would carry a little grain, his tools, and his beloved fiddle, and go off to hunt in the mountains by himself.

Alone and with no regular place to stay, he went on until nightfall and then stopped where he found himself, under a tall tree. There he lit a fire and cooked himself a meal. Then he took out his fiddle and began to play.

The night was soundless and the birds were silent; there was only the sound of Young Wang's fiddle and the echo from the valley, which made it sound even more beautiful. About the second watch some great thing—he could not see clearly what it was—began to approach him. About ten paces away it stopped, and Young Wang could just make out, by the light of the fire, a very ugly monster, with great hanging tusks and shaggy hair. He had half a mind to run away, but in the dark forest there was nowhere to go. So he put his sharp ginseng gatherer's knife close to him and went on playing his fiddle. After a while the monster gradually came closer and eventually sat down by his side. Young Wang suddenly seized his knife and stabbed in the direction of the monster's chest. The monster gave a scream and fled with a sound like the rushing wind. Young Wang did not sleep that night.

Early the next morning, when he had finished eating and was collecting his things, getting ready to leave, a girl approached him. She was like a fairy, with mountain wildflowers in her hair, which enhanced the beauty of her face. Young Wang thought to himself, "I've been hunting ginseng in these parts for several days, but I've never seen any human dwellings. Such a beautiful girl appearing in this huge forest—this must be the same monster in a different form come to do me some harm." By this time the girl had already come close and greeted him:

"My mother told me to invite our benefactor to come to our home."

Young Wang thought to himself, "I must have wounded the monster; now he wants to tempt me into a cave to eat me. But if I don't go, there's nowhere to hide. I'll go and find out what it's all about."

After walking for about a mile they came to a house under a great tree. At the doorway stood an old woman.

"I've brought our benefactor," said the girl, as she invited Young Wang into the house. The old woman told the girl to prepare some tea, but when it was brought Young Wang did not dare to drink it.

"Drink," said the old woman, who had seen what the young man was thinking. "We are not monsters. Come with me and you'll understand." She led him out the door to the huge tree, so thick it would take four or five pairs of outstretched arms to encircle it; but the leaves were already turning brown. She pointed to the trunk. "Look, that knife is yours, isn't it?"

It was the knife with which he had stabbed the monster the night before, and sap was flowing from where it had entered. When they went back indoors the old woman said, "We live under the shadow of that great tree, and it has always oppressed us. It drinks up all the rain and dew. But we could never do anything about it. You stabbed it to death and saved us from ruin. You are our benefactor—that is why I asked my daughter to invite you here." Young Wang understood and no longer felt ill at ease.

After they had eaten, the old woman told her daughter to clear one of the rooms so that the young man could rest. He saw that the room was clean and tastefully furnished, so he moved in.

More than twenty days passed. Then Young Wang thought to himself, "I can't just stay here. It has already become cold and I've found no ginseng. How am I to get through the winter? I must get back to my work." So he took leave of the old woman, who did not try to stop him.

"Take your brother to the garden to gather some ginseng," she said to her daughter. In the garden Young Wang saw a whole patch of ginseng which were bigger than any he had ever seen before. The girl then took him to a smaller garden, where he saw two even bigger ginseng plants.

"That one with six sets of leaves is my mother; the one with five is me." As she said this the girl looked at Young

Wang, then shyly dropped her head. "Don't touch it, whatever you do."

They went back to the other garden and spent the whole morning gathering ginseng of a size rarely seen. Then, while the girl was resting, Young Wang took the opportunity to go back to the small garden to see the two big ginseng plants again. He did not dare move them, but gently scratched around the one with five sets of leaves, revealing a root as thick at the top as one's thumb. He did not dare to go on and quickly put back the earth. When he turned around the girl was standing in the house with her hair all disordered.

"I told you not to touch," she said when he came in, "but you took no notice. See, do you think I look well like this?"

Young Wang was very embarrassed, for he knew he should not have touched the ginseng. They heard a cough and the old woman appeared.

"I saw what happened," she said. "It's clear that you two have a common destiny. Get your things ready, daughter, and go with brother Wang. In this way we can repay him the favor he has done us."

Young Wang was delighted at this. He was more than twenty years old, but there was no one to find a wife for him. Now here was a girl, like a flower, like jade, who was to be his wife. In his fondest dreams he could never have imagined such a thing. So he knelt down and paid his respects to his mother-in-law.

"Make haste and take up your wife's ginseng, and be careful!" said the woman. Young Wang took such care taking up the ginseng root that it was a long time before he had finished. It was as thick as a teacup and in the form of a human body. He took it back to the house and wrapped it up. The following morning he took leave of his mother-in-law and left the mountain.

At the market in Yingkow he sold the other ginseng for a great deal of silver. Then, highly contented, he made his way to his old home.

In the evening he opened the parcel and the girl came out, leaving only the skin of the ginseng. He took the girl's hand, so happy he could find nothing to say. Both of them were a little shy, but eventually Young Wang said, "Come to bed, young wife, this is our home."

From this time on they were a loving couple. They bought a house and land and gave some of their money to poor relations. Three years later they had two children, a boy and a girl, who turned out to be bright and lovable.

One day Young Wang's wife said, "Get out my ginseng skin. I want to see whether it has decayed." He got it out of a well in the back garden and found that it was just the same as it had always been. But when his wife took it in her hands the tears began to flow down her cheeks.

"Wife, you have been with me for three years and I've never yet seen you cry," said Young Wang in surprise. "What is the matter?"

"It's because today we have to part."

Young Wang seized her hand and then he too cried. "Don't leave me! If you go, what will happen to our children?"

"I don't want to leave you and the children, but our lovers' destiny is fulfilled and I have to go back. There is no choice."

They wept bitterly, reluctant to part. Finally the girl fed the children and, looking at them, sighed. As she took up the ginseng skin and prepared to leave, Young Wang held her and would not let her go. But the girl said:

"We have to part. Bring up the children well and my heart will be at ease." When she had said this she vanished.

THE NOVICE MONK

The old folk say that ginseng is not native to the mountains east of the pass, but came there from Shantung province.

Long ago, on Cloud Dream Mountain in Shantung there was a temple called Cloud Dream Temple, in which two monks lived, one of them a novice. The elder monk used to neglect his duties and did not bother about burning incense or reciting the scriptures; instead he spent his time in the plain below with evil friends. Each time he went away from the temple he would leave a great deal of work for the little novice to do, and if the boy got on the wrong side of him he would kick him for no reason at all. Sometimes he would even light a bundle of incense tapers and scorch the boy's scalp right in front of the image of Buddha. The boy was thin, and his face was sallow because of this treatment.

One day the monk went off to join his friends, and the boy went with an ax to cut firewood. Suddenly, from nowhere, there appeared a child about the same size as the apprentice himself, wearing a red apron, very lively and dancing about all over the place. The boy, who was lonely without any playmates, was delighted. The two of them soon finished all the apprentice's work and then played in the temple courtyard, singing and dancing. The little monk had never been so happy in his life.

After this, whenever the monk went down the mountain to join his friends, the child in the red apron would come and play with the novice, running off just before the monk was due to come back.

After a while the monk noticed that the boy's complexion had become rosy with good health, and what's more, whatever hard work he left him to do was always completed. "There's something behind this," he thought. So one evening he called the boy and began to question him, and the novice told him everything, from beginning to end. The monk was puzzled: what family in the mountains had a child with a red apron? It must be a ginseng spirit. So he took a needle out of a box and threaded it with red thread. This he gave to the boy and told him to pin it to the child's apron when he next came to play.

The following day the monk went off and the child came as usual to play. When suppertime came the child with the red apron said to the boy, "It's late, and time I left." The boy was on the point of telling his friend everything that was on his mind, but he was frightened of the monk's finding out, so when the child was not looking he took the opportunity to attach the needle with the red thread to his friend's apron.

The following morning the monk took a tool, quietly locked the door, and followed the trail of the red thread. Near a pine tree the needle was stuck into a ginseng plant. He was very pleased. He dug up the ginseng child, which he took back to the temple and put into a cooking pot, with a big stone on the lid to keep it down. Then he went inside, woke up the boy with a few cuffs and told him to go into the kitchen and light the fire.

The pot had been boiling for some time when the monk's friends sent for him to join them. He could not refuse, and as he left he said to the novice, "Don't you dare take the lid off the pot until I come back. If you do I'll break your legs!" After he had gone the boy kept the pot bubbling away; the steam kept rising and the whole room was filled with a wonderful smell. Curious to know what was cooking he lifted the stone from the pot cover. Then he took off the lid and got the shock of his life. Cooking away in the pot was a fat child! The fragrance filled his nostrils. The boy detached a piece of meat and put it into his mouth. What a good taste! He took another piece. It was even better than the first; then another, and another, and in no time he had eaten it all. Then he began to feel a little frightened. But thinking that there was no point in stopping now he plucked up his courage and tried the soup. Then he called the dog and gave him some; the rest he poured away around the temple.

He was just about to start cleaning out the pot when he heard the monk calling in the distance. Not knowing what to do, he took fright and ran away. As he did so he felt his feet grow lighter and soon found himself flying in the air, followed by the dog and the whole temple! When he saw this the monk realized that the boy had eaten the ginseng child. In consternation he shouted up to the novice, but the boy took no notice. When he called the dog it bit him, and the monk gave a gasp and expired. Then the novice, the dog, and the temple slowly rose into the clouds.

The child with the red apron was really a ginseng plant.

There had been two ginseng roots under the old pine tree and when one of them fell into the hands of the monk the other cried and cried, until one day the old pine tree said, "Don't cry, child. I'll take you with me and we'll run away."

"It's the same everywhere," said the ginseng child. "In any case I have not long to live."

"East of the pass in the mountains," said the pine, "there are few people and many trees. If someone should catch you there I'll protect you." So the ginseng child stopped crying and fled with the pine tree from Shantung to the mountains east of the pass, and settled down in the ancient forest in the Ch'ang-pai Mountains. Where else can the pine trees and ginseng in the Ch'ang-pai Mountains have come from?

Ever since, when gatherers dig up ginseng they quickly wrap them in a piece of pine bark to protect their legs and whiskers. So the pine tree protects the ginseng, as it promised to do long ago.

THE GINSENG BIRD

All the ginseng hunters of the Ch'ang-pai Mountains love the ginseng bird, because wherever he flies they know they will find ginseng. There is a story about ginseng birds which goes like this:

Once two families lived in the Ch'ang-pai Mountains. One was called Wang and the other was called Li. Both families had fled from the famine in Shantung province. Wang Gang, who was twenty-four or twenty-five years old slept on one brick bed with his mother, and a young unmarried man called Li Wu, who was eighteen years old, slept on another.

Although strictly speaking there were two families in the hut, in fact they were as one. Wang Gang and his mother had come from Shantung many years before. Li Wu had come more recently with his mother, his father having died of starvation; but she had fallen ill and died on the way. Left all alone, Li Wu had gone to stay with Wang Gang and his mother. They were related, so they let him live with them.

The two boys got on well with each other, and they became

sworn brothers and lived just as if they were real brothers. They were strong and healthy, and near their home they opened up some hill land and cultivated it. In the slack season they would either go hunting or else would gather ginseng. In this way the three of them made a fair living.

Eventually lumbering started in the hills where they lived and with the growing population the three of them found it increasingly difficult to make ends meet. The land they had cultivated was seized by officials and found its way into the hands of a rich landlord. Without any land to support them the two brothers went to the mountains as woodcutters. But the foreman was as fierce as a tiger, and they soon had to give this up and take to gathering ginseng in the mountains instead.

Now ginseng gathering is no easy life. They feared the foreman's temper, and to find ginseng they would have to search whole mountains. The shoots are so small and hidden so deep in the vegetation that finding them is like searching for needles in the ocean. They had to have good eyesight and patience. Then there was the risk of meeting dangerous wild animals. But they had no choice, for this was their lot. Although it was a hard and dangerous life, if they had the good luck to find one or two good ginseng roots they would at least be able to make a living. So they made their decision to leave and went to talk it over with Wang's mother. What could she say? She wiped away her tears and said:

"What fate is it that condemns us to such a bitter life? At home in Shantung we had roots and bark to eat, yet we managed to make do. I thought if we came east of the pass we could at least spend a few days in comfort. But the lot of the poor is the same wherever they go. If I stop you from going how can we live? Go if you must, but be careful." So they packed some food and other things that they needed and took leave of their mother with tears in their eyes.

The two brothers went deep into the mountains and found a spot to make a small shelter. Every day at dawn they would take some food and some tools and go into the mountains to search for ginseng. Only when the sun set would they return to their shelter. In this way more than a month passed, and it was almost time to go home. Their food was nearly finished, but with all their toil they had only found four or five small ginseng roots. Wang Gang began to get ready to go home, but Li Wu was reluctant to give up.

"It wasn't easy to get as far as this. We can't go back with only these few poor ginseng—we'll have come all this way for almost nothing. Let's stay a few more days and find some decent roots to take back."

Wang Gang had no answer to this and eventually agreed. So they stayed in the mountains and continued their arduous search over peaks and hills. More days passed, but still their situation was no better. Again Wang Gang tried to persuade his brother to leave.

"It looks as if we have no luck. We'd better go home, otherwise mother will be worried."

"Brother," said Li Wu, "I don't want to go until we have found some ginseng. Let's search for one more day, and if we find none tomorrow we can go home. I've had an idea: let's split up tomorrow, and perhaps that way we'll have more chance of finding some."

So the next day they each took some food and prepared to start their search. As they took leave of one another Wang Gang said:

"Little brother, you'll be on your own now, so mind you take great care. When the sun sets come back to the shelter whether you have found any ginseng or not."

"You take care too, and don't be late coming back."

So the two brothers made their separate ways toward the ancient forest in the Ch'ang-pai Mountains called the Forest of Oblivion. This time Li Wu did not search in vain, but found two fair-sized ginseng. Greatly pleased, he made his way back toward the shelter. "I haven't done badly," he thought. "I wonder how Wang Gang has done. These are two fine roots—I can't wait to show him."

The sun was about to fall behind the mountains, and the

forest was growing dark. Li Wu hastened back to the shelter. Wang Gang had not returned, and everything was quiet except for the cawing of crows in the treetops. Li Wu's high spirits faded away and he began to be anxious, wondering why his brother had not returned. Perhaps he had found some ginseng and had not finished digging it up? Or was there some other reason? He lit a fire and starting cooking some millet so that they could eat together when his brother returned.

Soon the food was cooked but Wang Gang was still not back. Although Li Wu was hungry he could not bring himself to eat. He kept thinking, "Why isn't he back? I hope nothing has happened." He sat down beside the fire to wait, increasingly anxious and distressed. After his day in the forest he was tired and without intending to do so he fell asleep.

Time passed, who knows how long? Then he heard a voice in his ear, saying,"Look, brother, look! What is this?" It was Wang Gang! Ah, how anxious he had been! How hard it had been to wait! He quickly stood up and ran to his brother's side. In Wang Gang's hands there was a large package wrapped in bark, such as ginseng hunters use to protect the precious root. It must be a fine mountain ginseng! How happy he was! "How heavy is it?" he asked excitedly. "Top quality," replied Wang Gang. "It's already in human form and about seven or eight ounces." Li Wu stretched out his hands to take the package and almost fell on his face. He woke up. It was a dream.

He rubbed his eyes, stood up and looked everywhere. There was no Wang Gang. The fire was already out and above the treetops innumerable stars twinkled. He listened. In the distance a deer called. He thought of his brother Wang Gang, and his heart ached. "I've come all this way with brother Wang hoping to find some ginseng to sell, so that the three of us could live in comfort. If he fails to return how can I go home without him? What can I say to his mother? No, I won't go home alone. I won't go home unless I find him."

Unable to sleep any more he put some more wood on the fire and sat down beside it. Then he heard a bird singing somewhere nearby. What sorrow the mournful song of the bird evoked! Had it lost a companion as well? Brother Wang has not come back. He wept in desolation.

The next morning as soon as it was light Li Wu took his staff and went into the Forest of Oblivion to search for his brother. Up and down he went, over peaks and hills, over rivers and torrents. Day after day he wandered through the forest. When his food was exhausted he picked mushrooms to eat. When there were no mushrooms he ate wild berries. His cowhide shoes wore out, his cotton-padded trousers were torn to shreds, his legs were tired and aching, and still there was no trace of his brother. The weather turned cold, the leaves went from green to yellow, from yellow to red. Soon the snows would come. Where is Brother Wang? He searched several hundred *li* of the Forest of Oblivion and still there was no trace of him.

Did Li Wu ever find Wang Gang? What happened to Li Wu in the end?

Some say that Wang Gang met a tiger and had been eaten, and that Li Wu, searching for him, died of starvation in the mountains. Some say that the brothers did not die, that Wang Gang was transformed into a mountaineer bird, Li Wu into a ginseng bird, and that in the evening they fly in the great forest of the Ch'ang-pai Mountains and as they fly they call, "Li Wu! Li Wu!" and "Wang Gang! Wang Gang!"

Whenever ginseng gatherers hear the sound of the ginseng bird, nine times out of ten they will be sure to find ginseng. Those who hunt for ginseng in the mountains always honor the memory of the two brothers.

THE OLD MAN WITH YELLOW HAIR

About a hundred and thirty or a hundred and forty years ago there was a man called Ho who lived in Shansi province. He used to hear the old folk say that "east of the pass there are three treasures." He did not know what the other two treasures were, but he knew that one treasure was ginseng, because it was said that if you eat it you never grow old. Ho always remembered this. When he had put together a little money he made his way to Jilin and looked for a friend from his own village.

He went to the region of Jiaoho and Dunhua to the southeast, and when he found his friend he did not want to do anything else but insisted on going into the mountains to hunt for ginseng.

At that time this region was still not opened up, and the mountains and dense forests were deserted. There were all sorts of alarming rumors about the many fierce beasts there, how tigers would tear a man limb from limb, how black bears would gnaw your face as soon as look at you, about wild boars in packs several hundred strong, which could crack a man's skull like a nut with one crunch of their jaws. Among the sea of trees in the dark forest you could not see the sun, you could not tell north from south, east from west. Even seasoned hunters would lose their way in these parts, and if they found themselves in the "Dry Rice Bowl" or the "Big Sauce Jar" there were only one or two chances in ten that they would ever get out again. So his friend urged him not to try his luck here, but to make a living somehow or other at home. But he had been thinking of ginseng for so many years and, like the heroes of old, he "refused to give up till he reached the Yellow River."

Ho's friend knew a very experienced ginseng hunter called Zhang, and he asked him to take them both with him. Everything was arranged and the group was formed. Ho provided himself with oil, salt, millet, and tools and set out with the others for the mountains. But after several expeditions they had not found a single good ginseng root. Even after the beginning of autumn they had little to show for all their work, but at least there was enough to pay for their necessities, and they had not worn out their shoes for nothing. The others saw that the season was finished and prepared to leave the mountains. But Ho, who had had such visions of finding some big ginseng and of being able to make his fortune and return home riding in a mule litter, was very disappointed. "I've reaped no grain and still have to carry the sack," he said to himself. Even the traveling money he had brought from Shansi was spent. It was like getting a rusty knife into a scabbard. He had heard that collecting mushrooms was a way of making a living and the season was at hand. It would be better to leave the mountains only when he had finished collecting yellow mushrooms. His companions saw that he was an honest man; out of pity they gave him their spare millet, oil, salt, and other useful things when they left.

He was alone. Every day he gathered stones to make mushroom pits and cut rushes to make baskets to carry them in. Sometimes he went higher up the mountain in search of yellow mushrooms. When the frost came he started gathering.

One day, at dusk, when he came back from the forest, he saw that the door of his shelter was closed. At first he thought that one of his former companions had come back to see him, so he went straight in. Something was lying on his bed—and it was very big. He stepped back in fright. What on earth was it? A man? Surely not—it was too tall and covered with hair. A wild beast? Black bears look a little like humans, to be sure, but the hands and feet were not those of a bear, nor the face. Tigers, wild boars, deer, leopards—none of them looked like humans. If it was a ghost—then he was just scaring himself, for he had never believed in ghosts. The shape of the body, the face, the hands and feet, clearly showed that it was human; there was nothing frightening about it. He had his sharp ax in his hand, so what was there to be afraid of?

"Who's in there? Come out at once!" he shouted, plucking up his courage.

"Me," mumbled a voice from inside. Then the bent body of a tall old man emerged. He was about eight feet tall, and had no stitch of clothing: his whole body was covered with yellow hair two or three inches long, and the hair of his head and beard reached halfway down his chest. He had a pleasant face and stood smiling at Ho.

Ho asked him who he was and what he was doing there. The old man said he lived not far away in the valley of South Mountain. He had stumbled upon the shelter, and thinking it looked like a human habitation he was waiting for the owner to return in order to ask him something.

"What do you want to ask?" said Ho.

"I wanted to ask if the Ch'in Emperor has finished building the Great Wall yet," said the old man. "Are they still conscripting men for the work?" Ho saw that there was something mysterious about the question, so he invited the old man into the hut and lit a pine taper. Then he asked the man the reason for his question.

"I come from the state of Yan," sighed the old man. "When Dan the Heir Apparent sent Jing Ke to assassinate the Ch'in Emperor, the plot failed and the Ch'in Emperor in revenge wiped out the six states and then immediately started to conscript men to build the Great Wall. I was afraid of getting caught so I ran off into the deep mountain forests to hide. From your accent you must be from the state of Wei. Are you hiding from conscription as well?"

Ho explained that the Great Wall was finished long ago and that the Ch'in Emperor had been dead two thousand years. "Several dynasties have come and gone since then and there is no longer any need to be afraid. Now it is the Ch'ing dynasty which is in power. So now that you have the chance, go back to your old home." But the old man was still doubtful. He could not believe that so much time had passed. How could it be two thousand years? He spoke of his bitter life—how, after he came into the mountains his clothes had gradually fallen to pieces and he had grown all his yellow hair, so that he looked neither like a man nor a ghost. He no longer dared to come out of his hiding place. When he was hungry he had only grass and roots to eat, and only water from the spring to drink. In this way, one way and another, the years had passed—who knows how many? Ho felt very sorry for the old man and tried to comfort him. He told him not to be sad, that he did not need to go back to his hiding place in the valley anymore. He could stay in the shelter for a while until Ho could find a way to take him down the mountain. Then he cooked some millet, and they ate it together.

The old man asked him what he was doing in the mountains. Ho told him how he had left Shansi to come there, how he had found no valuable ginseng and had decided to gather mushrooms instead. The old man asked him what ginseng was, and Ho showed him the few tiny roots he had found. The old man looked at them, then put one in his mouth and chewed it.

"I thought it was some precious thing or other," he exclaimed. "But it's just a root I eat every day. There's nothing rare about this; there's plenty in the valley where I live. But I don't bother eating such small ones as this. Tomorrow you can come and see."

Ho was so delighted that he could not sleep. He could hardly wait for the dawn to break. He got up and cooked himself some food, took two big tubs, tied a basket on his back, and set off with the old man.

The old man walked very fast and thought that Ho was dawdling, so he put him on his back and ran. They soon reached a cliff. Here he put Ho down and said, "It's down there." Ho took one look at the steep precipice and started shaking with fear. When the old man saw that he was afraid he took the basket and just jumped off the cliff. Before long he brought up a basket full of ginseng. They were superb mountain ginseng, thick as hens' eggs, with tight skins and fine wrinkles—not like homegrown ginseng. Ho was delighted. But it was a pity that the fine end roots were broken off.

"Never mind," said the old man. "I'll get you another basketful." And he went down again. This time he brought up a basket of ginseng with unbroken roots, but still without the whiskers. Ho explained that ginseng must not be pulled up: you have to scrape around it. He even drew a picture of how it had to be done. This time the old man was a long time gone, and it was evening before he appeared again. The ginseng he brought back had both whole roots and whiskers. Ho was very pleased and urged the old man to hasten back. The old man took the baskets, tucked Ho under his arm, and with great strides went back to the shelter, reaching it when darkness had just fallen.

Ho put the three baskets of ginseng carefully to one side, admired them, and felt he could not be happier. He then lit a fire and cooked a potful of millet as well as reheating what was left over from the morning meal. He ate four bowls full, but the old man ate a whole potful and still was not satisfied. So Ho cooked some more. After eating this too, the old man licked his lips and pronounced himself satisfied, then he drank all the millet water.

Ho thought to himself how much his three baskets of ginseng were worth. His friend had told him that if five or six men could find two or three shoots like this in a season it would count as good work. "And I have all this to myself! It's all thanks to the old man." To show his gratitude he told the old man that the next day he would go alone down the mountain and get some clothes for him. Then together they would take the ginseng to the market at Chuanchang and make an equal division of whatever they got for it. Afterward they could decide for themselves whether to go home or stay in Jilin.

The old man saw that Ho was a fair-minded man and was very pleased at the proposition, particularly as he had not expected anything for himself. Having made his plans, and pleased at the thought of doing a good turn for the old man, Ho had a good night's sleep.

He got up early the next morning and made a meal but did not wake the old man yet. When the meal was ready he called several times, but there was no answer. When he shook him he found that the old man was dead. For so many years the old man had been unused to eating cooked food. The evening before he had eaten several bowls of millet and had drunk all the millet water, so that while he was sleeping the grain had swollen in his belly and killed him. Ho thought of how good he was, of his strange life, and was struck with grief to find him dead. Now he could never repay the kindness the old man had shown him. But there was nothing to be done about it, so he dug a deep grave near the shelter and buried him. For a long time he remained very sad, and when he finally left he was still in tears. He cut himself a carrying pole, tied a basket to each end, and put the other on his back. Then, with mixed joy and sadness, he made his way back to his friend's home.

When his friend and companions learned that Ho had met a yellow-haired old man and had gathered three baskets full of ginseng they could hardly believe their ears. But when they saw the proof they cursed their own luck and reproached themselves for not staying with Ho. They all said that if the old man ate nothing but mountain ginseng it was no wonder he had lived for more than two thousand years. But if a meal of millet could kill him this was proof enough that there were no immortals in the world. Though eating ginseng can make one live longer, it cannot make one immortal.

Ho got his friend to accompany him to the market in Chuanchang. When the merchants saw how excellent his goods were and learned of their mysterious origin they treated him like an honored guest, gave him good food and wine, and entertained him. He exchanged the ginseng for a great deal of silver, with which he started at Chuanchang a medicine shop, which he called "Shiyi Tang," or World Record Hall. They say he chose this name in order to commemorate the yellow-haired old man, his benefactor, the oldest man in the world, and before long many towns east of the pass had their own Shiyi Tang medicine shops.

WANG HONG'S STORY

There was once a man of Hopei province called Wang Hong, an honest and virtuous man. He had only an old mother, more than seventy years old, and they were very poor. They only just managed to make ends meet and never knew where their next meal was coming from. They had a hard life.

When Wang Hong was sixteen years old there was a drought in Hopei and for three months not a drop of rain fell. The crops withered and died. Then there was a plague of locusts, and when that was over there was a flood. The village folk fled and were scattered—husbands separated from wives, children from parents.

Wang Hong's family had not one grain of rice and his old mother fell ill. What with sickness, hunger, and misery she got worse day by day. As she lay dying she took her son's hand and said through her tears:

"You cannot stay here, child. Go east of the pass and seek a living there." Then she died. Wang Hong wept and buried her. Before he left he went to her grave, and with an aching heart and tears in his eyes, he set out with a basket on his back and a staff in his hand, begging his way to the land east of the pass. In those parts, everyone said, there is ginseng, sable furs, and other medicinal herbs, and poor people can find a livelihood. But when Wang Hong arrived he found that this was far from true. There was nothing to eat, nowhere to live, his clothes were in tatters and he had no company except wolves, tigers, panthers, and insects. The life of a poor man was worth nothing. Who knows how many were frozen to death, died of hunger, or were eaten by wild beasts every day!

When he came east of the pass Wang Hong lived in the Ch'ang-pai Mountains. He built himself a shelter, planted some maize, collected medicinal plants and wild berries, gathered mushrooms, and once or twice every year he went down the mountain to the market and exchanged them for some salt, cloth, and so on. In this way he managed to eke out a living. Thus forty or fifty years passed and he reached the age of seventy without having very much to show for it. His clothes were tattered and patched.

Then one evening in autumn he sat on the edge of his brick bed smoking and thought of the old home he left so long ago. What was it like now? He longed for his home, but how could he go back there, with no money to his name? Just at that moment an old man with a white beard came in. He was clothed in green, and had a jar of wine in one hand and two pounds of meat in the other. In this lonely mountain forest how pleased Wang Hong was to see someone! He got up and invited the old man to come in and sit on the bed.

"Cook a little food," said the visitor, "and we'll drink a few cups of wine together." So Wang Hong cooked something and warmed the wine and they sat together drinking wine and chatting.

"I've been east of the pass for more than fifty years and have nothing to show for it. I would like to go home, but I haven't any money, so I can't."

"Don't worry," said the old man. "You'll soon be able to go home."

When they had finished the wine the old man got up to go. Wang Hong too got up to see him off. Once outside the door, in the twinkling of an eye, the old man vanished.

The next day he came again, once more with a jar of wine and two pounds of meat. Wang Hong cooked the meat, warmed the wine, and they drank together.

"I don't even know your name," said Wang Hong.

"My name is Sun."

"And where is your home?"

"If I tell you that you'll know who I am."

"Then tell me."

"I come from Laiyang and my name is Sun,
Across rivers and seas I seek ginseng.
For three days I only ate a crawfish.
Is that deplorable or is it not?
If anyone comes looking for me,
Look for the course of the Crawfish River."

Wang Hong was staggered. "You're an old ginseng hunter, are you?"

"I am," said the old man, with a laugh. "I saw that you were poor and in distress, and an honest man as well. So I'll give you a hand, and help you to get back home." When Wang Hong heard that he would be able to go home he was delighted.

"Prepare a peachblossom bow, a peachwood sword, and a willow basket, and tomorrow come with me. Whichever ginseng I tell you to dig up, don't say anything, but dig it up." Wang Hong willingly agreed.

The next day the old man came again, and when they had drunk some wine they tidied up and went off toward the west. After crossing three peaks they arrived at a piece of flat ground, and there was a whole fiery-red patch of ginseng. The old man told Wang Hong to take the biggest. But no sooner had he done so than from the west another old man appeared with bare legs and chest, and started to curse. "That ginseng belongs to someone!" Wang Hong was puzzled. If the ginseng belonged to someone why had they taken it? Yet the old man in green had said that Wang Hong must do as he was told. He shouted "Ginseng!" and the barelegged man immediately vanished. There on the ground was another large ginseng. Wang Hong tied it with a red ribbon, and taking up his peachblossom bow and peachwood sword, he dug it up.

Just then an old woman appeared, with disheveled hair, sobbing and sniveling, and cried, "That ginseng you're digging —it's mine! Go away!" Wang Hong felt a little sorry for her, but the old man in green had said, "It's a ginseng, dig it up!" So Wang Hong called out "Ginseng!" and the old woman immediately vanished. He looked down, and there was another large ginseng. So he dug it up.

He had just finished when suddenly a young man appeared. He was very sturdy and had a carrying pole in his hand. His face was full of fury, but he did not say a word. He was about to become violent when the old man in green pointed to him and said, "Ginseng! Dig!" When Wang Hong himself called out "Ginseng!" the young man disappeared as well, and there in his place was a large ginseng, which Wang Hong dug up too.

Then he stripped three sheets of bark and wrapped up the

three ginseng roots. The old man in green then pointed to other large ginseng, which Wang Hong dug up as well and wrapped in bark. Then he put them all into the willow basket.

"These are ginseng treasures," said the old man in green. "There are no merchants in Yingkow who have enough money to pay the price. Go and sell them in Jizhou in Hopei province." Then the old man in green disappeared.

Wang Hong returned to his shelter, found a large jar, and put the three great ginseng in it. Then he covered them with a false bottom and filled the jar with food. The other ginseng he put into a dung hod and covered with dung. This was a precaution against robbers. Then he prepared himself some food, took some grain with him, and, carrying the dung hod and the jar, went off.

He journeyed for two months, suffering extremes of cold and hunger, wind and rain, until he reached Yingkow. He sold the small ginseng to a merchant for several hundred ounces of silver, then took a boat for his old home. He was several days at sea and then had to travel for more than a month before he reached Jizhou in Hopei. Here he found merchants who knew the quality of his goods and could afford to buy. He sold the smaller of his three "treasures" for five *tang*. The "old man" ginseng he sold for fifteen *tang* and the "old woman" for thirteen *tang*. The merchant said to him, "The old man ginseng is a hulling-mill ginseng, the old woman is a flour-mill ginseng, the young fellow is a rice ginseng. If they are put in a granary the grain will never be exhausted."

Wang Hong took his money, bought a small donkey, and returned to his old home. The friends of his youth had all died of hunger or disease, or else had fled from the famines. He had no relatives left. It happened again to be a year of drought, the land was dry and cracked, and thirsting for rain. The crops were as dry as tinder. Country folk were eating grass and roots or the bark of trees, selling their children, or else taking their own lives or fleeing. Yet in the official granary there was plenty of grain. What could the poor do? Without money you died of hunger, and the officials did not care.

Wang Hong was very distressed to see this, and remembering how it was when he had left home, he wept. Knowing the suffering of the poor he gave away his own money. Those who had no money to buy grain, no money to provide for the sick, no money to buy clothes—they had only to ask him and he would give a few ounces, or a few dozen ounces of silver. He was a good man, who helped the poor at a difficult time.

THE WICKED UNCLE AND HIS NEPHEW

In Jinan prefecture in Shantung province there lived a rich man called Liu, whose home was in Liu village. Every year in the fifth month he used to go to the Ch'ang-pai Mountains east of the pass to hunt for ginseng, and he made a good living in this way. Rich Liu's elder sister lived with her sixteen-year-old son, Li Kwei. They were very poor, they had no land and only one room to live in, and they never knew where the next meal would come from. One year, before Rich Liu went off to gather ginseng, his sister said to him:

"Why not take your nephew with you? He can pay for his keep by gathering ginseng."

"All right, I'll take him," said Rich Liu.

So Li Kwei went with his uncle east of the pass to search for ginseng. In the great forests of the Ch'ang-pai Mountains they searched for more than a month without success. Very little was left of the millet they had brought with them. Rich Liu was very displeased. "That poor nephew of mine has brought me bad luck," he thought. He became angry and irritable and kept calling Li Kwei "good-for-nothing" and "ill-omened pauper." The lad felt very badly used, but he did not dare to answer back, so he was always very miserable.

One day his uncle said crossly, "We'll stay at home today." So they did not go out, and the uncle slept in the shelter. But Li Kwei was unhappy and could not sleep, so he wandered out. He had walked for quite a long time, climbed three mountains, and crossed three peaks, when he came to a deep ravine. He looked down and saw in a space about three paces across a great many blood-red flowers. He had never seen such flowers and thought to himself that perhaps they were ginseng plants. So he went back to the shelter and told his uncle what he had seen, and they went together to look. Sure enough they were ginseng, and of high quality too. But the ravine was several hundred feet deep and how could they get down? Li Kwei thought for a while and then said, "We can weave a rope out of rushes and let ourselves down."

So they went back to the shelter and made a rope. Then the question was, who should go down? Of course Rich Liu told his nephew to do so, so the boy tied the rope round his waist and went down into the ravine to gather the ginseng. There were a great many, and it took him three days to dig them all up.

His uncle hauled up the ginseng basket by basket. They were all of the first quality and one of them even weighed a pound! "Seven ounces is a precious thing, eight is a treasure" —and one weighed a pound! What a lot of money! The uncle began to plot mischief: he wanted all the ginseng for himself. So he hauled up the rope and called with false kindliness, "You stay there, nephew— I won't be long." So he abandoned Li Kwei, and taking all the ginseng, went back home even richer.

When he got home his sister asked him why her son had not come back, and Rich Liu replied, pretending to be distressed, "I'm sorry, sister, but I didn't look after your son properly. He fell ill in the mountains and died." When his sister heard this she fell into a dead faint.

When Li Kwei, down in the ravine, saw his uncle go he was very frightened. He cried out to Rich Liu to pull him up, but no one heard him, though the boy shouted himself hoarse. Night fell, and he was alone at the bottom of the dark ravine— a frightening place even in daylight. He was terrified, and, thinking of his home and his mother, wept tears of misery.

Three days passed. Li Kwei had nothing to eat and the

pangs of hunger were unbearable. Trying to find something to sustain him he went toward the east, searching, without realizing the passage of time or how far he had gone. Suddenly, in front, a great wind arose with a desolate whine. Li Kwei quickly hid behind a large rock and peered out. A huge python appeared, as thick as the mouth of a tub, its eyes like handbells! It came near to where Li Kwei was and then stopped. The wind dropped. As Li Kwei watched, the python flashed out its tongue and licked something twice, then turned and went away, once again with the sound of whining wind. As the python got farther away the wind got weaker. Li Kwei came out from behind the rock and went to the place where the python had stopped. There was a large ginseng growing there, blossoming with a blood-red flower. Imitating the python Li Kwei licked the flower. Strange—he no longer felt hungry or thirsty. Strength flowed into his body. "This must be a treasure," he thought. So he dug it up, wrapped it in pine bark and put it inside his shirt. Then what? He had a treasure, but he still could not get out of the ravine. Suddenly, as he pondered, he heard someone call to him. He turned and saw a young man of about twenty years, stocky and strong, and dressed all in green, even to his socks and shoes.

"What are you doing here, little brother?" asked the stranger.

"I want to go home, but I can't find the way."

"How did you get here?"

Li Kwei told him how he had come searching for ginseng with his uncle, who had abandoned him.

"Don't worry, little brother," said the young man. "I'll help you find the way." Li Kwei was delighted. He was glad to find a companion anyway, but one who could show him the way—this was almost too good to be true. So together they went eastward, and after a while they saw a great cave. "Let's go this way," said the young man, "perhaps it will lead us out." They went on and on, and eventually they could see light in front of them. Farther on they could distinguish the sky. The tunnel led from the bottom of the ravine out into the open at the top. Li Kwei was surprised and relieved.

"Now you will be able to find your own way. Good-bye." Li Kwei was sorry to see the young man go, but he could not very well force him to stay, so they parted. Then he suddenly remembered that he did not know the young man's name.

"Brother," he called, "we get on very well together, yet I don't know your name and I don't know where you live."

"That ravine where we were just now, that's where I live. My name is Mang . . ." Before he had finished a wind arose, and the young man vanished. Now *mang* means python.

Li Kwei sold his ginseng and returned to his old home in Shantung with a great deal of money. He reached home at dusk, went to the door and listened: there was no sound. "I wonder what has happened to mother," he thought, and tapped lightly on the door.

"Who's there?"

"It's me. Open the door, Mother."

"Don't scare your mother, child. You know I've got no money to spend. Tomorrow I'll borrow some from the neighbors and buy some paper cash to burn on your grave. Go back now, child."

"She must think I'm dead," said Li Kwei to himself. "Mother!' he called. "I'm your own son Li Kwei. I've come back. I'm not dead. Open the door."

His mother thought, when she heard this, "Perhaps he isn't dead then, otherwise how could he talk? All right, I'll open the door and then we'll see." So she opened the door, and when mother and son saw each other they fell into each other's arms.

Li Kwei told her all that had happened in the Ch'ang-pai Mountains, and his mother was pleased, angry, and full of hatred all at once. She hated her own brother for having the heart of a wolf and the lungs of a dog; she was pleased that her son had come upon good fortune in the end.

The next day Li Kwei's mother cooked several different

dishes. Then she went out and invited the neighbors, saying that her son had been dead some time but she had never held a funeral feast for him, so would they come today and eat a little just for the form? Rich Liu was also invited.

Everyone had taken his seat and they were just about to start eating when Li Kwei came in from the back of the house and bowed to his uncle and the neighbors. The neighbors were dumbstruck and did not know what to think.

"Don't be afraid, uncle and neighbors. I'm Li Kwei and I came back to Shantung yesterday. I have invited you to eat in order to thank you for looking after my mother."

"But we heard that you fell ill and died in the mountains east of the pass."

At that Rich Liu could bear it no longer. He got up, saying he had to relieve himself, then slipped away and was never seen again.

Li Kwei and his mother lived in comfort for the rest of their lives.

THE MOUNTAIN SPIRIT: KOREAN TALES *

André Eckardt (b. 1884) was formerly a Benedictine, and spent many years traveling and teaching in Korea. During that time he became an authority on ginseng and its place in Korean culture. He translated the following stories into German from the mouth of his Korean source, Kim Pong-che (1865–1932), "worrying," he says, "about phrases and dialogue."

The Korean ideograph "sam" (probably not related to Sanskrit soma, *the divine mushroom of immortality) has three meanings: "three," "Orion," and "ginseng." These meanings are explained and connected in the next-to-last story, "The Three Different Sons."*

* André Eckardt, "Der Berggeist," from *Die Ginsengwurzel,* Eisenach, 1955.

Inseparably linked to the sam *root is the veneration of the* sam *god, Sanson (or Samson) the Mountain Spirit, who holds a fundamental place in Korean myth and religious life. Ancient trees are especially sacred to him, and these are often surrounded with piles of stones and small coins placed there by the faithful as offerings. His devotees would sometimes build a small shrine nearby, in which there would be found a picture of the Mountain Spirit as a venerable old man, usually depicted with one of his feet laid on a tiger, surrounded by the ten symbols of long life.*

A shrine to the Mountain Spirit, before which is the ancient pine, sacred to the deity, surrounded with the votive stone pile. Photograph by André Eckardt from his article "Ginseng, die Wunderwurzel des Ostens," included in *Festschrift: publication d'hommage offerte au P.W.* Schmidt (W. Koppers, ed.), Vienna, 1928.

Two charcoal burners, Chung and Pak, took their brazier on their backs and went many leagues away from their home village of Hau Koka, in the province of Kyonggi. The road wound endlessly upward to the mountain pass. Often the two had to halt, for the burden pressed heavily on their shoulders and backs, and it became harder for them to breathe or even to speak; moreover they had to pay great attention to the road, which was everywhere steep, stony, and rough.

Finally they arrived at the high pass, the place where the half-decayed bough of an ancient pine towered into the air and a huge pile of stones surrounded the blasted trunk. People called it the ghost pine, and indeed it looked like a phantom tree. Both men, exhausted, sought shelter here. Each took a deep breath, spit, and threw still another stone on the ten thousand stones in the pile as a sign of devotion, then they sat down at a respectful distance from the ghost pine to smoke a pipe.

"May the great Mountain Spirit help us too in our poverty," murmured Pak, and spit once again, whether from despondence or from reverence it was not known, for saliva makes the breathing thick. It was ordered in the works of Yu Hang * that Yong Song should cherish his delicate breath in order to prolong his life, if he desired to nourish his spirit and become immortal. Deep in thought, Pak stared in front of him.

"I know a sequence of stories in which the sacred Sansonnim † gave us help, where he was not obliged to help us at all," said the reflective Chung.

"Of course! I have also heard many stories about the Mountain Spirit and I am eager to learn the ones you know. So begin your stories—you are the elder," said Pak, looking up at his neighbor eagerly, whose forehead, gray until then, looked sharply white when he removed his sooty headband.

Chung cleared his throat and reflected a while, then took

* The Korean name for Liu Hiang, a Chinese physician who lived *c.* 1000 B.C.

† *nim* is a suffix of respect.

an energetic draw on his bamboo pipe, until the cloud of smoke curled upon itself while rising in the air, and began.

THE GNOME

In the village of Won Byong there lived at one time two brothers, Kim Killyong and Kim Suryong. Their father had long since passed away, and his splendid burial had cost Killyong, the elder son, all of his inheritance, for it was the duty of the firstborn of the family to provide for the burial. It was a long time ago, also, that the *pak chung-hi,* the soothsayer, became uncertain when he tried to decide where the burial place should be, and extracted the last penny from Killyong's pocket. Killyong had to quit his house, and now lived in a wretched thatched hut on the outskirts of the village, together with his wife and his twelve-year-old son, Kaydong.

The younger brother was by comparison in full possession of his inheritance, and looked contemptuously on Killyong, who had fulfilled his duty as a son. Now and then Suryong would give a feast for his friends and acquaintances, or would invite them for a glass of *yak-chu,* the clear rice wine.

Such a day was coming again, and a great many guests were invited by the younger brother to a banquet. The friends were coming from far away, and only Killyong was not invited. He was very sad and sat in his hut, cold and hungry. His son saw this: it hurt him to the heart to see his parents hungry, forgotten, and cast off by his uncle. He slipped away from the house, hurried to the ghost pine, and offered a prayer to the Mountain Spirit to help his parents. He presented himself there as a sacrifice.

Then the boy distinctly heard a voice coming from the tree: "Follow me into the forest!" He looked about him but saw no one; only a glowworm, which flew in circles before his eyes and pointed the way into the forest nearby. Again Kaydong heard the voice and hesitated no longer, but followed the glowworm into the forest.

The path led at first over velvety moss, then over tree roots and undergrowth, through prickle bushes and tangled plants. Kaydong's hands and feet were torn with cuts, but the glowworm continued to fly ahead of him. The climb grew harder and steeper. Suddenly the little bug hovered over a wonderful ginseng plant, which lit up the gloomy woods like phosphorus. Then the glowworm's light went out, leaving no trace; Kaydong knelt to dig up the plant with the precious root. It was hard work.

Finally he held the golden-yellow root in his hand, and watched it grow larger until at length there stood before him a tiny gnome, who smiled at him and said, "You are a brave boy. Everything you have asked for in this place will be realized. You need only to strike this stick on the ground."

With these words he broke a branch from the nearest bush and gave it to the boy, who took it without a word.

"Ask for something, and show yourself that I have spoken the truth," said the gnome, encouraging him.

Kaydong struck the stick on the ground and said, "Dear Mountain Spirit, I ask that my parents may not go hungry."

And immediately there appeared a table with rice dishes and *kim-chi* * with fish, eggs, and a dish of fragrant ginseng.

"Eat first, to strengthen yourself, and take to your parents all that remains," the tiny man instructed.

The boy bowed low, then sat down at the table to eat. However much and however well he ate, there was no less food. Finally he stood up wanting to thank the small root-man once again, but he had already vanished.

Then Kaydong twisted the ginseng stems into a handgrip, tied it to the magic stick, and fastened it to the table. The glowworm appeared once more and led the boy back down to the ghost pine, where it disappeared; but Kaydong knew the way from there and happily hurried home.

How long he had been gone, he could not say, but his parents were extremely grieved, for in addition to losing in-

* A kind of turnip-cabbage, never absent from Korean meals.

heritance and standing, they now thought they had lost their son as well.

The homecoming was joyful; the food was brought forward and all the wondrous things were told, and the parents shed tears of gratitude and joy. Before Killyong would touch the costly dishes of delightful food, he made a low bow and said, "Dear Mountain Spirit, thank you for your help and mercy! This very night I shall come to your pine and make a sacrifice." Then he sat down at the table, ate, and was satisfied. His wife also ate, and her tears mixed with the *kim-chi.*

Soon the distress of Killyong and his family was ended, and again and again the boy and his father climbed up the mountain, whenever another wish was fulfilled.

Killyong's neighbors were astonished at how this man, from his bitter poverty, was suddenly in possession of wealth. Some said he had to be in league with the devil Ma-gui or with the Dog-gabi, the ghosts and household spirits; others said they had often seen Killyong and his son leave the house at night, and return a little later loaded down—most likely he had stolen his wealth.

It came also to the ears of the younger brother that Killyong, in a very short time, had once again come into all his property. His wife was filled with indignation, and was sure that this had come about only through theft from her storeroom—Suryong should soon and properly sound out his brother.

Indeed he sent for his brother, but the brother answered that in recognition of his newly regained standing, his younger brother might now come to him, and whenever he wished. Suryong became angry over this, but he had to resign himself, for he was indeed the younger, and in obedience to tradition and law had to oblige his elder brother.

His wife urged him on as well and was convinced that by inspecting the newly regained wealth of his brother, he would probably find something belonging to her, and could thus convict the brother of theft.

Suryong agreed, and proceeded immediately to his brother's house. His brother welcomed him without ill will, and led him into the guest room. In the center there was a gracefully turned charcoal brazier for pipe lighting. In the corner stood a tall candlestick of gold with butterfly wings, whose costly enamel shimmered in every color. On the dazzling, sparkling oil-paper floor were laid splendidly patterned mats and many-colored embroidered cushions. The walls were pasted over with blindingly white handmade paper. Killyong held out to his younger brother a long pipe with silver decorations, enamel-inlaid mouthpiece and bamboo stem ornamented with fire-writing, and asked about the reason for the unaccustomed visit.

The confused Suryong cleared his throat, for such wealth was not usual even in his own home, and indeed he was considered the richest citizen in a wide area. Finally he asked, as if he permitted himself the question, where all this wealth had been obtained.

Killyong answered openly, how as a result of their father's burial, undeserved poverty had set in on him, and his younger brother's neglect had afflicted him, how he had gone hungry and cold and had previously been close to doing away with his life. Then he told further, how all this had gone to his son's heart, how the son had offered himself to the Mountain Spirit as a sacrifice, and how they had been helped.

"Show me this mysterious place too," Suryong then said. "We are brothers, and we shall share our joys and sorrows equally."

"Good," said Killyong, and gave his brother a stick (though not his magic stick) and said, "Now I will tell you about the place, but not until midnight should you strike the stick against the ground of the ginseng plant!" That evening he led him just up to the thorny path to that place, and indicated the opening to him. Then he quickly went away and left his brother alone.

Suryong wandered here and there for a while in the woods, looking around him, until the full moon stood high in the heavens, then he moved nearer to the spot where Kaydong had once found the ginseng, and struck his stick on the ground, saying, "I wish for a lump of gold as big as my fist!"

In the same instant his fist, which he had involuntarily clenched while making the wish, became hardened into purest gold. He could no longer move it, not even to bend his fingers. However much he strained himself, it remained rigid. Then he threw the so-called magic stick as far from him as he could, and went back to his house.

His wife saw the hand and was at first stunned by the glittering gold, but when she saw the helplessness of her husband she felt pity for him and hurried to Killyong, her brother-in-law. He ordered her to go with his brother to the place in the forest, and appeal to the Mountain Spirit.

Once more it was midnight. Suryong and his wife climbed up the mountain. The moon shone brightly down, and they could distinctly recognize the hole where the ginseng had been planted.

"I implore you, great Mountain Spirit, take away this golden hand, and punish me for my hard-heartedness!" begged Suryong.

Then there came down against both of them such a hard beating that they dropped to the ground as if dead. Suryong held his healthy hand behind him, but he would never know anything more of gold or riches, and he was cured of his greed for as long as he lived.

From time to time there came to Killyong's house an old woman, nearly blind. When leaving one day she discovered the stick and mistook it for her own. But it was too weak and broke apart on her way, so she carelessly threw it aside. By this means Killyong finally lost the magic stick, but he did not lament the loss afterward, for he was by this time happy and satisfied, and as long as he lived he gave thanks to the kind Mountain Spirit.

Thus the charcoal burner ended his tale. His comrade had attentively heard him and nodded his head in agreement. Then he got up and said, "Your story is beautiful and instructive. In truth, whoever wrongs the O-ryun, the Five Respects,* deserves the punishment of Heaven. Today we must go home. But if my elder brother is agreeable, we shall rest here tomorrow, and again the day after, and tell one another our stories."

Chung struck his knee and said, "Indeed, we'll hold to this!" And both men took up once again the brazier with its heavy load, and trudged with measured steps down the mountain path.

The following day around evening both the charcoal men came again to the pass of the ghost pine. They spit and sat themselves upon a spur of rock within sight of the deformed tree.

Pak slowly filled his pipe and began to speak.

THE BEASTS' CAVE

When I look around us and see so many mountains, valleys, and fertile plains, I always think of one story, which has been repeated since the time of the Three Kingdoms on the Mount of the Waxing Moon. There lived in the village of Andong a married couple, who possessed only a cow, an ass, and a nanny goat.

One day the man said, "Whether we keep the goat or not is of no importance. I want to slaughter it and eat it up."

The woman loved her husband exceedingly and was blind to all his habits and sudden whims. She fed the cow and ass their little bit, but not the goat, and so went about her business.

One day the man said again to his wife, "Whether we keep the ass or not, what does it matter? I want to slaughter it and eat it up." And he invited his friends to come, and they ate the ass.

Again the woman spoke no word of rebuke, for she loved

* The Five Respects of Confucian ethics are: the respect between prince and subject, between married people for each other, between older and younger brothers, between superior and subordinate, and between friends in mutual business.

her husband and remained quiet before his wishes. As was her custom, she fed the cow and went about her work.

A few weeks might have gone by, when the man said, "It is of no consequence whether we keep the cow or not. I want to slaughter it and eat it up."

Now the woman was angry and said, "What do you mean, 'Whether we keep the cow or not?' Then what shall we plow our field with?"

The foolish husband did not listen to her, however, but slaughtered this animal as well.

When the woman saw that all her work had been done to no purpose, and that her husband had also squandered their tiny hard-earned savings, she wept bitterly and said, "Two of us cannot live without sustenance; I shall go out and work." And she went to the house of her rich uncle, winnowed grain, washed laundry, and looked after children. The uncle, a prudent man, commended her and presented her with a sack of rice. No sooner did night fall and work end, than the woman lifted the sack onto her head, hurried to her husband's house, laid the sack on the veranda and returned.

When the man saw the sack of rice the next morning, he rejoiced at the gift from Heaven. "What good spirit has made me this gift?" He thought of Mirok-posal the Savior, of the Mountain Spirit and the Spirit of the Seven Stars, but said to himself, "I have never made a sacrifice to any of these; why should they have helped me?" Finally his wife came to his mind, and indeed when he looked outside into the yard he saw a woman's footprints in the snow. He followed the tracks, came to the uncle's house, and saw how hard his wife was working. Then, without letting himself be seen, he returned to his own house and ate up the rice.

Again the weeks passed, and again the woman received a sack of rice as recompense. This time too she hurried to her husband's house and put the sack on the veranda. In a short time he had eaten up all that rice, without further concerning himself about his wife.

When she had taken a third sack of rice to her husband's

house and observed how he, thinking neither about her nor of their future, greedily ate up that rice as well, she returned no more to her uncle, but hurried into the forest to take her life. "For what purpose should I work and take such great trouble? All my toil and struggle fly away like dust in the wind. A man like my husband is not dear to me." Thus she spoke to herself, wandering lost in thought up the forest path, finally arriving at the ghost pine.

There a branch towered far up into the air; she immediately thought of using this to further her plan, pulled a shoot from a climbing plant and fashioned a noose. Then she heard a delicate voice, as if from a bird, "Come with me, come with me!"

Astonished and frightened at the same time, she dropped the noose and looked at the bough from where the voice came. Now she saw a magnificent bird, whose plumage was iridescent with every color. The bird flew up, around, from tree to tree. "Where can he be leading me?" thought the woman, and followed timidly, but inspired with new energy. The bird flew always on and on, and stopped eventually in the darkest depths of the forest to alight on an ancient tree. At its foot the woman saw a wild ginseng plant and was filled with joy, for its root guaranteed the fulfillment of all her wishes.

Again she heard the sweet voice, "Dig it up, dig it up!"

The woman knelt down and soon held in her hands a beautiful, old, and fragrant ginseng root. Carefully she laid the root aside, when it took on life, arms and legs, torso and head, became bigger and bigger, and finally a little boy stood before her in many-colored clothes, with a beaming face.

The woman didn't know if she was awake or dreaming. She had never seen such a beautiful little boy. "You always had the wish to be the mother of a boy. Take me with you. I will always be obedient to you, and whenever you have any wish, just tell it to me without hesitation."

The woman agreed to this and took the little boy as her own, though he immediately became the leader, saying, "This forest shelters many wild animals, bears, and tigers. I will lead you to a cave, but I will stay by you."

And just so, they soon came to a dark cave. In the back of the cave were piles of hay. There the woman made a bed, but the boy all at once turned into a fox, and said to her, "Keep yourself still and don't be afraid. The wild beasts will soon come together here. I'll stay by your side!"

The woman hid herself deeper in the hay and right away heard the rumbling of the tiger and the growling of the bear. Immediately the tiger became rigid, looked at the hay, and said, "Someone must be here. I have heard a rustling in the hay." He went over and pushed aside the hay with his paw and found the woman, who implored him tremblingly for her life. "Unggh," snarled the tiger, "I am very partial to human meat. You are welcome here."

Then the fox came out, laid his paw appeasingly on the tiger's foot, and spoke. "Don't! Certainly not! This woman can perform good and useful services for us. She can watch over our cave."

The bear was agreeable, so the tiger let the woman free, and she was allowed to live undisturbed in the cave.

They had meat and grain in great abundance, and one day, when the animals were sitting at a meal in the cave and eating heartily, the woman stealthily left the cave and went to her husband's house, to take him some of their plenty. Then she saw him amusing himself with a strange woman. Angrily she laid the sack she brought with her on the veranda and hurried back to the cave.

The next morning the man found the delicious meat and grain and immediately surmised that his wife must have set down this valuable present. Again he found the tracks in the snow, followed them and in that way arrived at the cave. No sooner had he stepped inside than the tiger caught sight of him, rushed upon the newcomer, and tore him to pieces.

To be sure, the woman bemoaned her husband's fate, but the fox comforted her and advised her that whenever she returned to her old house after that, he would be there to attend her.

The woman accepted this advice as well, and she was under the protection of the ginseng-boy—for the fox had again taken the form of a tiny boy—happy and contented to the end of her life.

Thus Pak the charcoal burner ended the story of the wild beasts' cave. In his passion for the tale he had even forgotten his pipe. Now he stuck it under his belt and stood up.

But Chung struck his knee and said, "Splendid! So the woman's good nature found its purpose, and the hard-hearted husband received his just deserts."

Both men again took the heavy brazier upon their shoulders and proceeded to make their way toward their village.

The following evening Chung and Pak, with charcoal on their backs, again reached the high pass and laid their wearisome burdens on a rocky ledge. They looked around, while each filled his pipe; then Pak ventured, "Today it is again my elder brother's turn to tell a story in the sequence. My story was about a devoted wife and the Mountain Spirit's help."

Chung sat down, cautiously kindled the fire for his pipe with flint and sponge, and began.

EVERLASTING LIFE: THE MOUNTAIN SPIRIT'S MAGIC

Yim Kyong-ubi was one of the most renowned generals of Korea. In the year of Mu-chin * he did battle bravely on the side of China against the Manchu. He became grievously wounded one day and was shaken with a violent fever. In his delirium he had a strange vision: the Mountain Spirit appeared to him with a message from Sang-che, the Lord of Life and Death, and spoke to him: "Because you have struggled so valiantly, I shall endow you with eternal life. But you must first win it for your children." Then the Mountain Spirit disappeared again, and Yim Kyong-ubi lay alone on his sickbed. Still the words rang in his ears, but the more he pondered them, the more peculiar their meaning seemed, and he knew of no explanation for this mystery. As he thought

* A.D. 1628.

most intently what the Mountain Spirit could have meant with the mysterious words that he must win eternal life for his children, it occurred to him suddenly that there are indeed ten things which guarantee a long, unending life, namely: Mountain, Water, Lotus, Day, Deer, Cloud, Condor, Bamboo, Tortoise, and Pine. And again he realized that indeed he had ten children, five sons and five daughters. Immediately the sense of the dark words became clear to him and he considered how he could get these things for his ten children.

Now he had only one wish, that he should become well, in order to obtain eternal life for his children. During his long sickness he reflected on all the individual feats he would have to accomplish, and allotted in advance to each of his children their essential characteristics. One thing he soon realized was that he had to provide his five daughters with the pine, lotus root, and bamboo, besides the water and clouds, while the other five essences would be appropriate for his five sons.

Time slipped by quickly, and Yim became well again. He had left his sons assiduously practicing with bow and arrow and exercising on horseback. For them he had determined the following: the first should go as a hunter to rove about in the mountains, the second to the king's field army to endure the heat of the day, the third should hunt for deer, the fourth should slay herons and condors, and the fifth would be dispatched to a Buddhist monastery, where he would care for the tortoises and serve in the sanctuary.

And for his daughters he laid out a beautiful garden: the pines alternated with lotus pools and groves of bamboo, a waterfall rustled in the midst of the garden, and wild, rugged clusters of rocks towered upward to the clouds. He instructed his sons besides to capture animals alive and let them roam freely in the garden. Thus he created a small Paradise and believed that he had thereby fulfilled the will of the Mountain Spirit.

Parents and children lived happy and contented, and Yim thought that surely half the labor was done and the only inescapable condition for the attainment of eternal life was met. Each of his children soon had a favorite plant or a special animal in the garden, which was well-nigh as dear to each of them as life itself.

Then a terrible raging plague came over the whole land, and in a few days all the general's children had fallen victims to the pestilence. But then a wonderful thing came to pass: each of the children was transformed into his or her special plant or animal—the one each had so gladly protected and cared for in life—by the Lord of the Spirit World. And thus the garden remained, truly enchanted. Even to their greatest old age the mother and father came day after day to the garden, and their enchanted sons came to them and took food from their hands, and their enchanted daughters heard their beloved words and replied in the sound of rushing waters, in the gentle rain falling from the clouds, through their perfumes and the sweetness of their colors.

Once a year, however, on the anniversary of their enchantment, they were all permitted to take on their previous human forms, and then for one evening in the house of the happy parents there was loud rejoicing and a ringing, joyful feast. The merry guests thought not at all of the spell, but it was always there in their presence, in that they believed, in their happy spirits, that the banquet evenings with Yim Kyong-ubi were the brightest and happiest of their lives. They thought that even the king himself would hold it an honor to be invited to the house of his former valiant general.

In this way the vision found its fulfillment, and Yim Kyong-ubi was to his greatest old age thankful to the Mountain Spirit for this undeserved grace.

The narrator had no sooner finished, than Pak merrily concluded, "Oh, that I also might be endowed with such a Paradise."

Master Chung agreed with him and both men, all the while thinking of the magic of the Mountain Spirit, again took up their heavy loads and hiked downhill toward home.

On the fourth evening both charcoal men again appeared

at the pass. Arriving at the place of the ghost pine, they set down their oppressive load. Then, following the old custom, they threw a stone on the ten thousand others, spit, for they truly considered spit to be vital energy. It is written in the book *Li Ki* that Confucius himself uttered the maxim, "Whoever nourishes himself with breath glows like a god and lives long." And is not spit the condensation of breath?

Again both men took from their belts their beloved bamboo pipes, carefully packed the finely shredded tobacco into the tiny bowls and kindled fire. Then Pak cleared his throat and said, "Today is my turn in the order of telling. Listen, then!"

THE GOLDEN EGG

In a very ancient time, when the kingdom of Puyo migrated to the kingdom of Kokuryo,* there lived in the district of Changsong, in the modern province of Kangwon, a married couple who, because they were childless, lived from day to day discontented with the workings of destiny. But while the woman went about her daily work and so tried to get over her sadness, the man, named Kim Subaki, was morose and sullen.

They possessed, besides a mule, only seven hens. One day the man had a craving to eat a hen with his bowl of rice, and he said, "Whether we own seven hens or six, what great difference is there between seven and six?" And he ordered a hen slaughtered.

The woman objected to nothing, for she respected her husband and was aware that she had to be submissive. This was indeed one of the precepts of the O-ryun, the Five Respects.

It was only a few days later when Master Kim again said, "Whether we have six hens or five, in the long run it's the same; there is no great difference between the numbers." And again he ordered a hen slaughtered.

* The kingdom of Puyo in northeastern Korea lasted from 1286 to 59 B.C., the eastern kingdom of Puyo from 59 B.C. to A.D. 494, and Kokuryo from 37 B.C. to A.D. 668.

The woman was sorry, for she thought of the eggs, but in the end she made no objection, and the hen was killed.

Not even a week went by, and Master Kim said again, "Whether we feed five hens or four is just about the same, for the difference between five and four is trifling." And he ordered another hen slaughtered.

By this time the woman had become a little exasperated at the behavior of her husband, and she made bold to object that very little more than half of their original number of hens was left.

The man replied, "It is written by Kuan-tse,* 'Throw away your "I" and be quiet, then godly purity will remain preserved in you. Whoever thoroughly understands silence and stillness understands the basic texture of Tao.' "

At these words the woman held her tongue and sacrificed the fourth hen.

But Master Kim was not contented. With words from the traditional scriptures he would again and again suppress the restraining reluctance of his wife, and so in the course of time one hen after another was slaughtered, until only one was left.

"Whether we keep one hen or none, is there any difference?" asked Master Kim, and ordered that the last hen be slaughtered.

Now the woman became really angry and said, "Man, have you no thought for the coming day? Now you will have no hens left, not even an egg. What do you intend to eat?"

The man, however, replied, "I heard Confucius, the master, speak from Heaven how Chuang-tse in his first book informs us that the fulfillment of one's duty is not to his advantage, and does not keep him from harm, unless he is silent, and in this way walks above the dust and slime. So be quiet and do what I say."

Now the woman, who was versed in the Han-mun, the Chinese writings, and was also skilled in traditional scriptures, became angry and replied, "When my husband cited the phi-

* D. 645 B.C.

losopher Chuang-tse just now, he might also have added that the wise man continued from there and said, 'Confucius himself considers these words to be foolish talk.' " And she raised her eyes to Heaven and entreated, "Gracious Mountain Spirit, make my husband's nose long, so that he may perceive the foolishness of his behavior. And give enough to me, that we may have what is needful for daily life."

And indeed the unheard-of came to pass: Master Kim's nose grew longer and longer, so that his entire face was deformed. It was wider than the door, indeed perhaps it was growing taller than the door, when the woman cried out (though not from compassion), "Sanson-nim, stop, stop!" Only then did the nose stop growing bigger; but the man had such a long nose that he had to hold it with his hand, and when he sat down he had to prop it up on a wooden stand. Everyone who saw it laughed at first and then, touched with pity, wept for him.

Secretly the man sent for the *uisa,* the doctor, to have the nose cut off. The *uisa* attempted it, but under his hands it started to grow again and became even bigger than before. Then the terrified doctor said, "Master Kim is possessed by angry spirits; whoever associates with him will become infected." He ran from the house and never appeared there again.

Now Master Kim called in the *pak chung-hi,* the magician, but with all his talk and pretense he couldn't make the nose any shorter and quickly left the house, so as not to suffer loss of face.

When the woman came to the kitchen and slaughtered their last hen, she found inside it a golden egg. Her joy and surprise were inexpressible, and she said nothing to anyone about her discovery and their good luck.

Gradually the man's understanding became clearer, and he implored his wife, "Manuranim, ask your protecting spirit to restore to me my nose and my judgment." And he promised never again to neglect the needs of daily life with all his studies.

The woman replied that she must first make a sacrifice to

the Mountain Spirit. Yet in her heart she said, "If my husband is restored again too quickly and regains his normal nose, perhaps he'll be no better." And she unkindly exposed him further to the unpleasantness of the long nose and to everyone's ridicule.

A few days later she made a pilgrimage to the ghost pine and placed a straw man, in which she had wrapped an egg, on the stone pile at the foot of the tree, made profound obeisance three times, gave thanks for the golden egg and asked for the recovery of her husband. Then she went back to her house, blindfolded her husband, and touched the golden egg to his nose, which now slowly shrank, and soon assumed its former shape.

Then both lived on in happiness and contentment. In spite of the golden egg the woman did not become presumptuous, but worked just as she used to, and respected her husband as long as they lived.

Thus Pak ended his tale of the Golden Egg. Chung grabbed himself by the nose, to make sure he had his own normal one, then struck his knee and said, "By her good sense and her reliance on the protecting spirit, she healed her ridiculous husband. By the way, your tale bears many a likeness to the one about the beasts' cave of the day before yesterday."

"Yes, so it does," agreed Pak; then both men lifted their loads of charcoal on their backs and set off from the mountain pass toward their village.

The next evening both came again to the high pass and laid their brazier by the ghost tree, made a sacrifice to the Mountain Spirit and, as usual, sat down to rest on the rocky ledge and produced their pipes. Pak said to his comrade, "Today I'm eager to know what story you'll tell. I told the tale of the Long Nose last night to my wife and children, and they couldn't stop laughing all night."

Chung laughed too, and after clearing his throat, began his story.

THE BOY'S SACRIFICE

In the province of Kyungsang * the small city of Yongyang lies at the foot of the mountain called Irwolsan. In an ancient time there lived in that place an honest and industrious family, consisting of three members, an old father, burdened with worries, a sick mother, and a tall and slender boy, nearly thirteen years old.

Every day the father would go out to cut wood. Whenever he reached the first height of Kogay, the level part of the pass, he would pause, as we do ourselves, to stand for a moment before the ghost tree. Then he would throw a stone or a small copper coin on the pile and sigh, "Lord Mountain Spirit, make my old woman healthy again." Then he climbed higher, deeper into the forest, and worked till evening when, loaded with wood, he would start for home.

But in the narrow hut his wife became sicker and sicker. Many doctors called, only to leave again, for none knew the way to help the woman. All the medicines used turned out to be worthless. Finally an old and experienced doctor and magician declared, "When the only son sacrifices himself, only then can the mother's sickness be healed."

Everyone in the house became frightened and gloomy, yet the boy, young as he was, remained calm and said that he would gladly offer a sacrifice of his life if his mother would then become healthy again, but he asked for a delay of three days in order to be of service to his father in the woodcutting.

On the third day the boy again accompanied his father into the woods. When they came to the high pass, he felt so tired that he asked his father to let him stay behind and rest a bit. The man gladly agreed to this, and the boy lay down in the shadow of the ghost tree and went to sleep.

Meanwhile something very strange happened at the father's house. The mother lay moaning in pain on her hard bed,

* In southeastern Korea.

when a boy came to the window, looked into the room, stepped inside and went up to the sick woman. "Mother," he said, "I am ready now. You can let me be put to death, and prepare the required medicine when I am dead, according to the doctor's words."

"By no means!" replied the mother. "I would rather die than sacrifice my only, beloved son. My sickness is beyond help!"

The woman found the boy's bright face very extraordinary, and the longer she watched it the brighter it shone, until her son stood before her, more beautiful and graceful than ever. Since his mother would no longer make the sacrifice, he tried to urge it upon her but couldn't persuade her again.

Into the middle of this affectionate argument stepped the doctor, who tore the clothes from the boy's body and threw him into a cauldron of boiling water. The boy became smaller and more wrinkled, a delicate smell of ginseng wafted from the cauldron, and the viscous mixture became as red as blood. The doctor forced the woman to take the curing medicine. No sooner had she taken it, than her real son rushed in the door and cried out, "Mother, here I am, accept me as a sacrifice!"

Both the woman and the doctor were terribly frightened, for now for the first time they suspected that a ginseng boy had come in place of the real son and had given himself as a sacrifice. And from this hour the woman was entirely cured and thanked the Mountain Spirit on her knees for her deliverance.

On this day the father came home earlier than usual with his load of wood. The son was explaining how he had had a strange dream, and all those present urged him to tell more, so he began: "Today I was a great deal more tired than usual. I could hardly keep up with Father's steps. When we finally came to the Kogay, even with the best intention I could go no farther, so I lay down in the shadow of the ghost tree and soon fell asleep. I dreamed that lovely birds were singing, and a very beautiful boy with a golden face, red shorts, and a purple jacket came up to me, remained standing before me, laughed and spoke. 'I love you very much; wish for anything and I will give it to you.' I never thought twice, but said, 'My mother is extremely ill. If I am allowed to ask you for one thing, it is this: make my mother well.' The boy nodded and answered, 'You are a brave child! Because you have asked for your mother's health, and not for money or positions of honor, I will not only grant your wish, but will also make you extremely prosperous. I will go myself and heal your mother of her sickness.' Then the little boy hurried away. I heard again the beautiful birdsong and then I woke up. I was completely light at heart. Now, Mother, when I see you well, I am truly happy for the first time, for now I know that it was not a mere dream, which never finds fulfillment, but the voice of the Mountain Spirit." And he kissed his mother.

Now everyone was happy, and the father hurried off to bring his thanks and worship to the Mountain Spirit. The mother also, when she became stronger, made a pilgrimage to the ghost tree. And the son became one of our most famous writers; his fame has lasted to this day and his name is on all lips: this was Kim Sayong who called himself Kim Antong.*

No sooner had Chung ended the tale of the Boy's Sacrifice than Pak, approving of it, said, "I think the mind of that fine boy is really admirable and his reward is well deserved."

And satisfied with the boy's fortune, both men took the load of charcoal onto their shoulders and started on their way back to their village.

When on the sixth night the charcoal men came again to the ghost pine and sat down, Pak began his story.

THE ARTIFICIAL JEWEL

A poor merchant named Kang Tadshol had found in the mountains of Chi Risan a precious mountain ginseng and had sold it to a sick Chinese for an equally precious jewel. He

* Mid-fourteenth century.

then delivered the jewel to his assistant, Yu Tongsik, with the request that he take it to Kang's wife, because Kang had much business to attend to.

Yu Tongsik carefully examined the polished jewel and thought to himself that it was easily worth a hundred pieces of gold, and that it could gain him a carefree life. He decided therefore that he would not hand over the jewel, but would keep it for himself and sell it at his leisure.

When the merchant returned home a few months later, he immediately asked his wife how the jewel had come to her.

"What jewel? I know nothing of any jewel! For months I have received no communication of any kind from my husband," replied the woman.

"So you got the jewel and sold it, or kept it for yourself, instead of using it for our subsistence," said the angry merchant. His wife still swore to the truth of what she said and almost convinced her husband, so that he hurried at once to Yu Tongsik and rebuked him for having kept the jewel for himself instead of delivering it.

"What are you saying?" replied Yu. "I certainly delivered the jewel. The two Ministers, Cho and Pang, are witnesses to that." In the meantime Yu had bribed these ministers to bear witness for him and exonerate him. Protestation stood against protestation, and Kang no longer knew whom to believe.

Now it was the custom in Kokuryo in the time of King Chung Su that every citizen of the country who had any entreaty to make should pull a bell cord in the hall of the royal palace, and he would be admitted to the King's presence.

Therefore the merchant went to the hall of the royal palace, pulled on the bell cord, was actually admitted to see the King and respectfully presented his petition.

The merchant's wife had meanwhile in her anguish hurried to the Donang Tang, the little temple of the Mountain Spirit, had donated a few grains of rice as an offering and begged for help. Worse than the loss of the stone for her was her husband's mistrust.

When the King had heard the merchant's petition, he sent for the two ministers. Each of them declared that in fact with his own eyes he had seen Yu deliver the jewel to the merchant's wife.

Kang heard this testimony and was very sad, for he loved his wife sincerely and could not believe that she would behave so disgracefully toward him. But there was now no doubt, and he was determining to send her away and part with her forever, when he had a strange experience. On the way from the royal palace to his home Kang had to cross through a thick forest. Suddenly a *taram-shu,* a black squirrel with a white throat, ran down a pine tree, stopped before the merchant's eyes, looked at him candidly, and said in a kindly voice, "Follow me!" The astonished man followed the lively little animal and soon came to a mossy spot, in the middle of which grew a splendid five-leaved ginseng, just like the one he had first found in the Chi Risan.

Delighted, he dug up the root. Suddenly there stood before him a tiny gnome who said to him in a clear voice, "Your wife is loyal, you can believe her. You were betrayed by your friend Yu, who has secretly buried the jewel. Have faith in my help." No sooner had the gnome said this than he vanished into thin air, the same way he had appeared. Only a pale ray of light remained on the place where the ginseng man had stood, the air smelled sweetly of ginseng, and the plant was in the same place as before, as if it had never been dug up.

None of the people involved could sleep that night: the matter would not leave the King's mind, especially since he had observed the merchant's sorrowful face as he went away, and he thought about how he could verify the ministers' testimony; Yu feared that his buried jewel would be found and his betrayal thus emerge; the two ministers were anxious lest their false testimony might be disproved before the King; the merchant thought about the meeting in the forest; the woman was conscious of doing no wrong, and resolved to serve her husband even more faithfully than before—in short, the traditional saying,

All things have a root and a top,
All events an end and a beginning;
Whoever understands correctly
What comes first and what follows
Draws nearer to Tao.*

will prove true this time as well.

The morning arrived. The King summoned everyone before him and again had the events reported, then ordered the people isolated, each to be led to a separate chamber, each to be given a piece of molding clay with instructions to reproduce the shape of the jewel. For the merchant this was an easy job; Yu also had long and attentively examined the stone, so he was able to reproduce its form without difficulty; but the woman had never seen the stone, so she could not make a model of anything; only the two ministers were uncertain and alarmed. Minister Cho made a round stone for, he said to himself, the stone was scarcely polished at all; Minister Pang made a stone with six sides for, he said to himself, most polished stones have this shape.

Then everyone involved appeared again before the King, and he inspected the shapes they had made. The modeled pices of Yu and Kang were eight-sided and identical to one another, but those of the ministers were quite different. The King immediately perceived that the ministers had committed perjury and ordered them, as well as the swindler Yu, arrested and locked up.

Then the merchant told the story of his experience with the ginseng root and the gnome. The King congratulated Master Kang and said, "You have a precious jewel for your wife, for by her loyalty and reverence she caused the noble Spirit to act, so that the truth has now come to light."

On parting the King asked Kang to bring him a mountain ginseng, in case he ever found another. The happy merchant hurried from there into the forest, to the place where the squirrel had led him, dug up once again the precious ginseng

* From the classical book *T'ai Hio* (The Study of the Ancients), attributed to Confucius, chap. 2.

root and thankfully took it back to the delighted King. This King had a long and beneficial reign, and his memory lived long among the people. Kang and his wife had no trouble greater than this for the rest of their lives, until they peacefully passed away.

Then the charcoal man was silent.

Chung slapped his knee in approval and said, "I don't know which I admire most—the woman's trust in the Mountain Spirit, the wise circumspection of the King, or the kindness of the ginseng gnome." Then he took the heavy burden on his shoulders and both men, thinking of the events of the story, went slowly down the mountain.

On the seventh day the men came to the high pass and sat down to rest on the ledge of rock. Now it was Chung's turn again, and he began to tell his story.

THE THREE DIFFERENT SONS

There once lived in the village of Mokpo in the province of Cholla a mandarin who had three sons, Hoasok, Pangsok, and Tosok. The eldest was fifteen, the youngest eleven, and the middle son thirteen years old. They were one in heart and soul and were always together, so people called them "the triple constellation." Their father and mother educated the boys in the best possible way, they had them instructed in the classical writings, and their father trained them besides in archery.

One day the three inseparable boys agreed, "Whichever of us catches or finds the most beautiful or valuable thing, no matter whether it be plant, metal, stone, or even a living soul, and brings it home with him, he shall be our prince for a whole year and we others will obey him." They made a formal pact, each cutting himself slightly and pressing his bloody hand on a roll of paper. Then they separated. Hoasoki * went to the left, Pangsoki to the right, but Tosoki was completely

* In Korean, *-i* is the nominative form, used for proper names.

undecided and finally went straight ahead, deep into the forest.

Pangsoki was the first to have an adventure. While he wandered here and there, thinking of yesterday and tomorrow he heard a faint whimper, but saw no one and didn't know if the noise came from a man or an animal. He followed after the sound, and in a bamboo thicket found a man, all bloody and with torn clothes, lying there helpless and moaning. The man's eyes were closed, and he was apparently near death. Pangsoki bent down in order to find out the cause of the injury and saw to his sorrow that no recovery could be expected. Then the wounded man opened his eyes, saw the boy's tearful face, and spoke, "I was attacked by men who knew that I had hidden in this forest the treasure of my parents and ancestors; they tried to force me to reveal the hiding place of this treasure. I resisted as well as I could, but their strength was too much for me, and I was beaten half-dead. My name is Kim Kyos-ubi and I come from the village of Andong. I live all alone; my wife and children were carried off by a plague; I have no one to offer a sacrifice for me at my death."

Pangsoki stayed by the side of the wounded man, gave him a little of the arrack which he carried with him in his gourd, and spoke to him dearly, as far as he was able to in his childish innocence.

"You are still young," replied the dying man weakly, "but as wide as the sea, as high as the mountains, as deep as the valleys and woods, just so wide and great is your heart already. Now I feel that I must die; I beg you to provide for my burial. I will tell you in return the place where I kept the treasure hidden." And he told him exactly about the spot, so as to exclude all doubt. The boy promised to fulfill everything exactly, and with a thankful smile the poor man died.

Pangsoki covered up the body and went at once to one of his father's tenants who lived near at hand, and gave all the instructions for a fine funeral. He also promised the man a rich reward if he conducted the ceremony in accordance with tradition, provided for a solid coffin and a good grave mound, and every year on that date made a suitable offering to the spirit of the deceased.

The tenant agreed, and the boy knew by this time that everything was in the best of hands, so he returned to the forest and looked for the spot that the dying man had described. It was a dark cavern, known to the people as a *horangikul,* a tiger's den, and always avoided. But the man had assured him that no tiger or other wild beast lived there now and that he could enter it without fear.

Nevertheless the boy did not feel quite at ease entering the dark and clammy cave; though he was not afraid, still it was something new and odd for him. The deeper he went into the cave the more he became accustomed to the darkness, which began to diminish a little where the sunlight shone into the interior through several clefts in the rocks.

After some wandering around, the boy came to a small, dark lake at the bottom of the cave, on whose bank he found a small boat moored. He untied it and rowed, as he had been directed, to the opposite bank, then stepped through a crevice into a second, bigger cave, which led at last to a stalagmite cavern. Who could ever describe what he saw there? Stone columns gleamed in every color, some towering free, some reaching up to the ceiling, some peaked, some twisted. Shapes of spirits and men, of animals and plants stood everywhere—in short, it was like an enchanted world. He had never seen or heard of anything like this before, it was so glorious. And indeed this cave was only a few hours away from his native village. Was he dreaming, or was it real? The rock and stone figures were white as marble: there sat an old man with a long beard, here a gnome imitated a hare, across the way was the entrance to a palace or temple with immense stone columns; on his left he saw a woman who was nursing a child, on his right he caught sight of a tiny petrified lake, out of which rose a flower. All was vast and phenomenal, still and lifeless. Then he called out his name in the stillness, to make sure that he really was awake, and became frightened, for from all sides rang out loud and clear, louder even than he had shouted it himself, "Pangsoki, Pangsoki!" Then everything was as before, still, forlorn, and lifeless.

Now the boy began to be really afraid. What if he could no longer find his way out of the cave, and froze to death there? And then he noticed that he was very cold. He wanted to go back, when the hidden treasure came to his mind. It must be found nearby. The man had said to him, to the right of a column sat a nodding old man with a long beard. He had seen him already! And under him lay an iron box, turned back to front. Pangsoki went over to the petrified old man and after moving aside several stones he actually found a great chest. He opened it and thousands of jewels, golden ingots, and ornaments of every kind lay heaped up inside, so much that he couldn't possibly carry it. He took from the chest several pieces which glowed like fire and seemed to him especially valuable, also some gold, closed the chest again, and set out for home. "My adventure," he said to himself, "is surely the most beautiful. I'm very curious about what my brothers met with."

And with joy in his heart he crossed the cave and found himself again in the forest.

In the meantime his elder brother Hoasoki had likewise gone deep into the forest and roamed aimlessly about, picking berries and shooting a few birds from their branches, when suddenly a beautiful young deer stood before him, eyed him guilelessly, and finally with a whimper, lifted up one of its feet. Hoasoki saw in it the long, sharp thorn of an acacia tree. He was sorry for the animal and with a jerk drew the thorn from its flesh. The deer lowered its foot and snuggled unafraid up to the boy's side, as if to tell him that it would always follow him. Hoasoki fondled and stroked the animal and gave it some of his provisions to eat. Wherever he went the deer followed him and stayed faithfully by his side.

Now it happened that he came near a well-hidden tiger trap and was very close to falling into the pit. The deer had sensed the danger and pressed itself so hard against Hoasoki that he was alerted and finally when the animal took fright even more as it glimpsed the trap, he recognized the danger and was able to avoid it.

Farther along there lay close to the edge of the path a poisonous snake, which had the exact appearance of a twisted root. The boy almost stepped on it and made it attack. Again the deer sensed the danger and pushed its master out of the way.

Hoasoki then saw the snake and as it reared up, about to attack the deer, he struck the serpent on the side of the skull, smashing it. He then broke off the fangs and collected the poison which he knew was used as medicine and was very valuable.

As Hoasoki strode on and had almost left the forest behind him, the deer halted and looked up into a tree. The boy at first saw nothing peculiar there and wanted to go on. But the deer held him back, and then he saw a magnificent phoenix with dazzling plumage. Hoasoki bent his bow and shot the bird, for the feathers were a precious prize and were paid dearly for.

With the deer as a faithful companion, the costly serpent venom, and the precious plumage of the phoenix in his bag, Hoasoki started on his way home and believed that he alone would carry off the prize.

The eleven-year-old Tosoki had also gone deep into the woods. He thought about this and that, considering what he could do to bring home something precious, but nothing out of the ordinary occurred to him. He thought about the berries of the shrubs and the fruits of the trees, about rare flowers and choice edible mushrooms, of birds in the trees and beasts in the woods that he could shoot. Because he was skilled with the slingshot he wasn't frightened at the thought of a battle with the tiger, the king of beasts, or with a bear, in order to get their valuable skins, but nothing whatever appeared, everything was motionless, quiet, and deserted.

The evening drew near and Tosoki still had had neither adventure nor valuable catch. Sadly he sat down on a stone covered with moss and lichen and thought and thought. How long he sat so, he couldn't tell; finally he felt so sad that he began to cry and thought himself inferior to both his brothers. Already he renounced all preeminence over them, all distinction, and resolved to return home empty-handed, when through an opening in the trees he caught sight of the constellation Orion with the three stars, the "triumvirate," in the middle, tranquilly shining down on him.

It occurred to him that this constellation always had a direct connection to the ginseng plant, with which it shares the same ideograph, as well as with the Mountain Spirit, Sanson-nim. He involuntarily clapped his hands and entreated, "Great Sanson-nim, if I am worthy of it, show me the way to find something precious."

Then he seemed to hear a rustling in the branches behind him; as he looked around he saw a tiny boy step forward with a face which shone like gold. The gnome stood before him, scrutinized him for a long time, and then said concisely, "*Dara-onora,* follow me!"

Tosoki wanted to ask him many questions, who he was, where he came from, where he was taking him, but the little gnome strode ahead so fast that he was hardly able to keep up with him and sometimes ran the risk of stumbling and falling over the gnarled tree roots or the stones in the dried-up mountain brooks.

The path led constantly uphill, and finally they arrived in the middle of a clearing before an ancient ghost tree, around which lay a pile of stones which in the course of decades and centuries the passersby had thrown there in veneration of the Mountain Spirit. The boy stayed a moment before the curiously shaped tree, which was half dead—apart from the hollow trunk only a couple of branches towered into the air. The pale moonlight fell so that there appeared on the ground the shadow of a man with a long beard. Thus Tosoki came to understand the long worship of the tree: the ghost tree could be only the magic transformation of a human being or the seat of a divinity.

The gnome disappeared, and the boy was alone once more. Why had the ghostly boy appeared and led him here? What was there to look for or to gain? He knew nothing and again felt alone and abandoned. Sadly he sat down on a tree stump near the ghost pine to consider everything again from scratch. Now the constellation shone brightly directly over the ghost tree, with the moon above the three stars. Unwittingly the boy wrote with his index finger in the sand at his feet the Chinese ideograph for *sam* and the number three (参), which signifies both "Orion" and "ginseng plant." Then Tosoki remembered a remark of one of his teachers, that in ancient times at the point of the three beams had stood the character for "heart." Only kindess of heart had the power to lift men up to heaven. He was very young, and he loved Chinese writing, which is more expressive and rich in pictures than almost any other writing in the world. But how exactly this ideograph had gotten the meaning of *sam* (ginseng) was still unclear to him.

As the boy bent down, suddenly the little man stood before him again, exactly on the spot where he had written. The gnome looked at him and again said only the word, *"Dara-onora,* follow me!" and walked ahead of him into the woods, which had now become even thicker and more impenetrable than before.

Again they stumbled for a while through darkness and thickets and over sticks and stones. Then the magic gnome suddenly disappeared and in his place stood a single radiant ginseng plant, brightly illuminated by the light of the full moon. The boy's breath stopped short for surprise and joy. He dug up the plant and held the golden-yellow root in his hand. Head and body, arms and legs were so clearly shown that one could think only of an enchanted root or a transformed human being. The face was full of wrinkles, so the root looked like a gnome.

Now the manlike form in his hand began to speak in a soft voice: "Know that on the day of your birth I was planted here as the seed of my lord and master and now I am exactly as old as you. According to the will of your lord and mine you have found me here today. This happiness is not the lot of tens of thousands of mankind. Therefore keep me as your protective spirit. And should you have any wish at all, whisper it in my ear, and I will fulfill it, as far as I am able." Then the root ceased and remained silent.

Tosoki requested the root to say the name of his lord and master, but the ginseng continued to be silent.

Happily the boy turned to go home, the ginseng root in his hand. He would prepare a place of honor in his cabinet for the precious root and resolved to venerate it as his protective spirit.

The following morning the three brothers Hoasok, Pangsok, and Tosok met on the *maru,* the veranda of their house. Then their father joined them and said, "Hoasoki has told me of your agreement, so give me an account of what you've experienced and show me what you've brought back."

First Hoasoki, the eldest of the brothers, with the deer by his side, began his account, then laid on the ground the snake poison and spread out the phoenix's splendid plumage. Everyone marveled at his exploits and at the costly things he had returned with.

Then Pangsoki stepped forward, recounted his meeting with the man who was fatally wounded, and showed the glittering gold and jewels. Again everyone wondered at the boy's nobleness of mind and at the treasure he had acquired. They were also amazed and thrilled by his description of the *sok-kul,* the stone cavern, and they decided they would accompany Pangsoki there.

As Tosoki, the youngest, was then only able to produce his ginseng root, the two elder brothers broke out into loud laughter; but their father remained serious, reproved them for their rash laughter, and encouraged his youngest son to tell his adventure.

Tosoki recounted everything truthfully, his sadness, his prayer to the Mountain Spirit, and finally his meeting with the ginseng gnome.

When he had finished his father awarded him the prize. The two elder brothers were astonished and stared at each other; then their father spoke, "Didn't you hear that the ginseng boy said to your brother, 'Should you have any wish at all, whisper it in my ear, and I will fulfill it, as far as I am able?' Now then, my son, ask the ginseng boy for some precious snake venom and for phoenix feathers!"

Tosoki whispered the wish into the shriveled ear of the root, and instantly there appeared before everyone's astonished eyes twice as much medicine and an even more beautiful set of plumage.

"And now wish to the ginseng gnome for gold and precious jewels."

This wish, too, Tosoki whispered into the ginseng root's ear, and quick as a flash everything appeared before them in even greater quantity.

"So you see then," the father concluded, "that your brother has obtained the finest, best, and most precious thing. There is nothing he can wish for that he will not receive. The ginseng root is plant, man, and spirit at the same time, the most precious treasure of all!"

Then the two elder brothers fell at the feet of their youngest and pledged him their obedience.

But Tosoki bade them rise and said, "I owe this good fortune only to my trust in the Mountain Spirit. We'll stick together and do honor to the name people will give us, the Ginseng."

"Excellent!" concluded their father. "And whenever you have sorrow or affliction, then raise your eyes to the stars! The triple constellation of the heavens shall be your goal and model. It is prescribed in the *Book of Changes,**

> Heaven lets its pictures hang down,
> Blessings and disasters to reveal.
> Accomplished men take the pictures as models."

Then the three brothers lived together in harmony and

* Appendix 3, *Hi Tse I.*

were worthy of the reward of being taken up among the stars.

There the charcoal burner ended his tale.

Pak clapped his hands and said, "Indeed, he spoke the truth! Our destiny lies in the stars."

Both men again took their heavy brazier on their shoulders and jogged on with measured steps toward their native hearth.

When the two men came to the high pass on the eighth evening, a gentle rain was falling. They halted in spite of it and presented their customary sacrifice to the Mountain Spirit. But it was too chilly for sitting and resting, so they walked together to and fro, unencumbered by the burden they had been carrying, while Pak began his story.

THE LONG EARS

In a very ancient time, when men did not shrink from murder, a King of Puyo had grotesquely long ears—so long that he would not venture out of the palace, and no man, with the exception of his near relations and a single minister (who had come and gone freely at the palace since his father's time) was permitted to approach the King.

Every month a young man was chosen from among the people by lot and taken to the King, but it was never seen that any boy ever again came back to his father's house. And no one learned why only young men were singled out, and no children, girls, or women. In every family where there lived a young man over eighteen years of age there was constant sorrow and dread that he too might become a sacrifice to the King's favor.

Indeed one day a messenger from the King came to the house of a poor widow, whose only son was the staff of her old age, and summoned the young man to follow him to the royal palace. The mother implored the messenger not to do this, and the son also advanced all the arguments he could, but all their entreaties were in vain. The envoy insisted that now it was indeed the turn of this family and this young man, and he would have to follow him; otherwise the King's displeasure would fall on the mother.

When the young man, Poknagi by name, heard this, he urged his mother to offer no more resistance, but to let matters stand for now. "Give me only until tomorrow morning," he said calmly to the King's messenger, "then I will be at your and the King's disposition."

Moved by the entreaties and the promise, the messenger consented and said, "Well, be it so. I will come back at daybreak tomorrow; for when the sun is high in the heavens, you must appear before the King."

After the messenger had gone, mother and son considered what was to be done to escape the impending fate.

"I will take a dagger with me," said Poknagi to his mother, "and when danger threatens me I'll kill the King; then our land will be delivered from the threat that all the young men will be chosen by lot and never return."

"Do not do this!" retorted the mother. "The King's person is holy, and the gods will avenge the deed!"

"Then I will implore the King to spare me because of you," said the son.

"When you discover why you are summoned by the King, you can perhaps give good advice," observed the mother, and continued, "You are suffering in this way because of your age and are afflicted by our destitution. Perhaps our protective spirit will give you justice."

They consoled themselves with this thought and parted. The mother went into the forest by the pale light of the moon, sacrified to the all-powerful Mountain Spirit, and prayed for her son's life.

Then a tiger appeared and did not fall upon the woman, but growled softly as a greeting and then spoke, "Do not be afraid, I will not hurt you. I am the servant of my lord and am to tell you that you will be freed from trouble. Your son will be advised; my master will give him the right words to say." Again the tiger growled, a very powerful fellow, and went on into the forest.

The woman went calmly home and recounted everything

to her son, who was then entirely confident about letting himself be led the next morning to the palace of the King of Puyo.

When he arrived there the boy was first given a silken gown to wear, then was regaled with a delicious meal, and finally they conducted him before the King.

The King looked at the boy for a long time, not saying a word. Finally he commanded, "Whoever you may be, you must give me a haircut. And so that you will tell no one that my ears are as long as donkey's ears, you will be doomed. But first you may express one wish. I have it in my power to fulfill one wish for you." Thus spoke the stern King, and handed the boy a hair-cutting tool.

He took the tool, then bowed low and said, "Royal master, I am not worthy to cut your hair, for when your messenger came to fetch me yesterday I first conceived the plan of bringing a dagger with me to kill you, but my mother persuaded me not to, saying that I would dare the wrath of the gods by laying hands on your holy life."

"Your mother is a loyal woman; I will reward her!" said the King.

The boy, however, continued: "You are shy to show the people your ears, and that is why you kill all those who see you and cut your hair. Might I be permitted to offer you some advice?"

"Speak!" the King encouraged the young man, whose open, fearless behavior impressed him.

And the young man said, "Oh King, order that a cap be made for your—as you call them—donkey's ears, so the ears are entirely covered up, and decree that everyone who comes before you must wear a cap just like it. This hat will become a great style in a short time, all of the people will be wearing such a cap, and it will not occur to anyone to ask afterward why this style was set."

The King found this suggestion very intelligent and said, "Your advice is good and I will follow it. I shall spare your life; you will be allowed to stay by me; you must promise me only one thing: that you will never say a word to any man about my ears. Do you promise me that?"

Poknagi gladly gave his agreement and assured the King that he would never say anything to anyone, whomever it might be.

The King therefore ordered a cap to be made, of white silk trimmed with black fur, which hid both his ears. The cap had the appearance of a helmet, yet was open at the top, so as not to interfere with the topknot of hair. A strong silken cord connected the two sides from front to back. The cap pleased the King exceedingly, and he gave the order that everyone who came before him, whether minister or simple countryman, should wear this cap, only they would use simple woolen stuff instead of expensive silk.

It wasn't too long a time before all the people at court wore such a cap. The people from the city and countryside saw them and made their own caps, for the style pleased everyone very much, and they were (this was the decisive thing) an effective protection in winter from the fierce cold. The cap could easily be hung up by the cord that held both sides together. In short, it came into general use and remains so even to this day.

"How excellent!" broke in Master Chung. "So we owe our wonderful hat to the king with the long ears. We should be very grateful to him!"

"Yes indeed. And now I'll go on."

One day the King became deathly ill. No doctor or magician knew the remedy for him or could help. Finally an old and experienced scholar was called in. When he entered the sick chamber he demanded that Poknagi, who always stayed by the King's side, remove the King's cap. When the young man explained with the pretense that this was impossible, the wise man urged him to tell the true reason. Mindful of his promise, the boy declared it to be the King's strict order never to remove the cap.

"Then it is very difficult to help him," said the gray-haired doctor. "The only remedy, finally, is a true wild mountain ginseng root. The King must drink a thick porridge of it and be rubbed with its juice. But where to find a real ginseng root? It is the pledge of long life, even of immortality. To be sure, only a noble and unselfish man, who is prepared to sacrifice his life for others, can find such a root. Where, then, is such a man?" And sadly the old doctor went away.

Then Poknagi was sad too. The phrase, "Where is such a man?" would not leave his mind. He pondered the question at length, thought of his friends and kindred, but not one of them would do, apart from his mother, whom he knew to be without a fault, and whose unselfishness was as high as the mountains of home and as wide as the sea in the distance.

So Poknagi decided to seek out his mother and consult with her about how they could find a genuine mountain ginseng.

His mother heard with inward sorrow of the King's dire sickness and the doctor's words. She would never have dared to think that she was unselfish. "I've always done my duty," she said simply, "but I have a vague recollection of some phrases my father impressed upon me:

> Nobility embodies human kindness and is therefore uppermost among men.
>
> Nobility unites so much excellence that it fulfills the rules for living and the *Li,* the good form of life.
>
> Nobility works such charity in creatures that it harmoniously unites the *I,* the duties of life.
>
> Nobility is unshakably solid; therefore it can accomplish great deeds.
>
> Nobility acts on those four qualities of which the *Book of Changes* speaks, the creative, incisive, generous, and imperturbable qualities; for creativity is the chief quality of human goodness, an incisive character is the epitome of excellence, generosity is the harmonious unifying of the rules for living, and imperturbability is the basis for all actions.

Poknagi was speechless. He had never known this side of his mother; she had never spoken in this way. So she knew the classical writings! And yet she had always remained so simple, quiet, and modest, and had worked night and day as a woman of the people, as if all this were a matter of course.

Then the woman told her astonished son about the Mountain Spirit's voice, which had spoken to her through the tiger, saying that she would be free from worry. "Without any doubt," she continued, "you too will be protected by the great Mountain Spirit. Therefore go quietly into the forest by moonlight and look for the root."

Partly in fear, partly in joyful confidence, Poknagi set out that same night and went into the forest, without really knowing whether he should turn right or left.

The moon shone pale, and the branches and trunks of the trees threw phantom shapes onto the mossy ground. Everything was living and moving. The wind whispered softly, and the shadows on the forest floor scurried here and there. Sometimes the young man was not sure whether he was dreaming or awake, or whether he had already entered the spirit world.

How long he went on in this way and where he was, he could not have said. Suddenly there stood before him an immense tiger, who growled, looked at him guilelessly (as if the animal were an enchanted human being) and spoke: "Do not be afraid; I am the constant attendant of my master and his messenger to those men who merit my gaze. I also know what has led you into the forest at this hour: it is the life of your king, whom you wish to help. He can only be helped if a man sacrifices himself for this purpose."

Poknagi did not know what was happening to him, or who inspired the words he then uttered, "I am ready to sacrifice myself!" He was alarmed by his action: it was as if he had fallen into a violent waterfall, and the whirlpool had carried him to unknown depths. He felt giddy and instinctively grasped hold of the nearest tree trunk.

Again the tiger spoke, "Do not be afraid! I will lead you to my lord and master, and he will decide whether he accepts your sacrifice or not."

And the tiger turned and went still deeper into the woods. The path led uphill through darkness and thickets, but finally they arrived at a large open place, in the middle of which was an ancient oak. On all sides stood the beasts of the forest: there was a row of tigers and leopards, one of deer and bears, one of hares and foxes. The constellation Orion shone brightly down; the moon lit up the meadow and made it into a fair-ground. Many-colored birds flew about, and merry songs and calls resounded in the still of the night. Whichever way the young man looked, dazzled by the beauty of the scene, everywhere were flowers of all colors, and besides the whole clearing was bordered with wonderfully fragrant shrubs, tufted with flowers. The air was full of the subtle odor of gin-seng: the precious plants were all around, their five-leaved crowns on high, slender stems, and by their number dem-onstrated their intimate community with the ginseng god.

The tiger led Poknagi through the rows of animals and plants. It seemed to him that they all bowed their heads to him. Both went along on the soft moss and arrived at the throne of Sanson the Mountain Spirit, a venerable man with something like a crown on his head and long, richly folded garments with wide sleeves in wonderfully shimmering silk. He held a fan in his hand, and his eyes shone with great benevolence. The tiger, who was, as it were, his watch in the mountain forest, lay down at his feet.

The throne stood directly next to the old ghost tree; here it was a gnarled oak, whereas usually the pine was favored as a symbol of long life.

The young man didn't know what was happening to him. He flung himself down and touched his forehead to the soft earth, then remained kneeling and scarcely dared to raise his eyes to the Spirit of the mountains and forests.

"I know your wish," the kindly Spirit began the conversa-tion. "Before I help you, you must answer me three questions.

The first question runs, 'What is the highest thing in this world?' "

The young man, who had reverentially laid his hands on his knee, answered, "The highest thing in this world is the worship of Sang-che, the Lord of Heaven, in whose authority you are sitting here."

The Mountain Spirit nodded and asked again, "And what is the best thing in the world?"

Poknagi did not reflect long on this question either but said, "The best thing is the practice of virtue and the control of passions. We read in the book *Li Yun,* 'Man's duties are paternal love, submissiveness, and a child's other duties toward his parents; the gentleness of elder brothers toward younger ones, the obedience of younger brothers to elder brothers; a husband's sense of duty toward his wife, obedience on the wife's part to her husband; benevolence on the part of older people toward younger people, docility of the young toward their elders; the sovereign's philanthropy, the subject's loyalty. These are the duties of man. He who practices them has chosen the best way.' "

Again the Mountain Spirit nodded, and looked benevolently at the young man at his feet. "And now the third question: What is the most beautiful thing in the world?"

"Noble Spirit," answered Poknagi, "what is there more beautiful than here, in your presence, to enjoy the beauty of the heavens by night under the stars, and before them all the radiant Orion, to enjoy the sweetness of nature with all her plants and her sweet fragrance, the birds with their song and the diversity of the other animals."

The young man was silent, and the venerable Mountain Spirit on his throne nodded approvingly. "You have passed the test! Because you have not praised human goods such as food and clothing, honors and prestige, health and wealth, but have seen that the superior goods are the highest, best, and loveliest, so you will be rewarded with the highest distinction and raised to the highest dignity. You will obtain the best healing ginseng and with it be able to cure your king's sickness. You will also receive a most beautiful reward, to see your mother for a long time healthy and happy. And now I shall give you as a pledge of my love a forest ginseng, which you will present to your king."

Once again Poknagi bowed down to the ground, then he took with both hands the golden-yellow ginseng root the Mountain Spirit handed him. With that he was dismissed. He threw himself to the ground for the third time; when he raised his head he found himself alone in the open, mossy clearing.

The ghost tree still stood a short distance away, the constellation Orion still sparkled in the southern sky, and the moon shone softly down; but the throne with the reverend Mountain Spirit, the animals, and even the ginseng plants had entirely vanished.

Had everything been a dream, then, or was it reality that he had experienced? Poknagi could not himself have said, but he held in his hands the gentle-smelling, golden-yellow root with its arms and legs. Fondly he examined the root and thought he detected in the wrinkled head at one time the laughing face of a child, at another the kindly expression of the venerable Mountain Spirit.

With the precious treasure in hand, the young man hastened downhill, and although he followed no path he soon arrived at the mountain pass, and from there went on to his village.

His mother welcomed him joyfully and listened with boundless astonishment to her son's story. That her only son should have partaken of this happiness and distinction was a great comfort to her and pure maternal joy. By the same token the son was extremely happy to be able to thank his mother in this way for her loving sacrifice and great devotion.

The very next morning Poknagi went to the palace and in the presence of the King handed the astonished doctor the healing wonder root. The *uisa* prepared the root, gave the thick mixture to the dangerously ill King to drink and rubbed its juice, which from steaming had turned blood red, on the face and body of the sick man. And the thing which no one had dared to hope then came to pass: the King soon became well again and was able to attend to the business of his kingdom.

The young man, however, of whom he had grown very fond and to whom he now owed his life, he made his prime minister and chief counselor. The people respected and valued him in spite of his youth, for he was as wise as an old man, as circumspect as an eagle, as firm in his resolve as a tiger, but also as kind toward everyone as a father.

Both Poknagi and the King remained thankful until the end of their lives to the great Mountain Spirit.

Master Pak ceased speaking and his comrade was silent for a long time. The story had moved him deeply. After a while he struck his knee approvingly and said, "This Poknagi really outdid himself; his spirit offering was royally rewarded!"

Although Pak was in a hurry to start, Chung remained sitting and sketched in the sand at his feet with his long pipestem the Chinese character for "spirit" (仙), saying, "Now it's become clear to me why this character is composed of the two characters 'man' (人) and 'mountain' (山): it's evidently the character for 'Mountain Spirit,' whom the boy revealed in all his excellence." And thinking deeply, he added, "What would happen if we ourselves, after all, were one day to go in search of a mountain ginseng? For days now in the presence of the ghost pine we've told of the most wonderful accomplishments of the Mountain Spirit and his root, and of the hope this kind-hearted god bestows on those who venerate him—nearly incredible, from what we've heard. We're poor, too, and trust in his help. Why don't we set out tonight in search of the *san-sam,* the mountain ginseng?"

"*Kurosumnita!* So be it!" affirmed Master Pak, "and the benevolent Mountain Spirit will be merciful to us!"

The two charcoal burners made their way down the hill, their burden on their backs. When it was growing dark, a brilliant moon shone in the heavens, and to the south the radiance of Orion moved up in the night sky. The two worthy men once again approached the ghost pine, threw a stone on the others as an offering, spit out of respect, and set off into the deep woods.

And in truth they found two beautiful, undisturbed, old mountain ginseng roots, and returned happily home. The ginseng gnome had not really shown himself, but the shape of the ginseng left no doubt that they had found genuine wild roots, which guaranteed health and longevity, and would help to brighten their poor hard lives.

Lure of the Ginseng: Hunters of the Taiga

"Taiga" is a Russian word and refers mainly to the vast evergreen forests of subarctic lands in Eurasia similar to those in North America. In Manchuria and southeastern Siberia, where the climate is not so cold, more deciduous growth occurs, and here flourishes the ginseng. The root plays a part in the medical arts of several of the native Manchurian tribes, including the Gold ("Fishskin Tartars"), Orochi, and Udege. It has traditionally been sought after, however, by the Chinese, and for the several centuries since deforestation has made the ginseng vanish from China proper, Chinese hunters have braved the taiga's trackless vastness and wild beasts to find the root, always extremely rare, making a small profit by selling what they find to the merchants of the cities to the south.

These men have found no chroniclers among their own people, and it has remained for Westerners, mainly Russians—travelers, explorers, "white hunters"—to tell of the hardships of the ginseng seeker's life. Indeed there are few reports even from this source. The Russians rarely spoke Chinese, and their interpreters, often Cossacks stationed in the Russian colonial settlements in Manchuria to protect the Trans-Siberian Railway, were perhaps not trustworthy—their cruelty certainly made them feared by the Chinese of the taiga. Yet if the Russian explorers' reports are less than reliable in detail, their curiosity and admiration cannot be gainsaid. They recognized the bravery of the Chinese hunters and the hazards against which they struggled. And they sensed that the search for the ginseng root meant more to these men than the possibility of small monetary gain: they were the purveyors of the miraculous, living among spirits and demons which protected the ginseng as well as those among its seekers who led honest and upright lives.

THE HUNT FOR GINSENG *

THE HUNTERS

The plant's rarity, and the high price for which it is sold in China, have produced a special type of ginseng hunter. In general they are people with neither hearth nor home, who come from the interior provinces of China, or natives (of Manchuria) who, to earn their livelihood, have had to live in the remote forests. Many ginseng hunters perform the trade from their infancy and continue to do so until extreme old age. They are recognized by their dress and equipment: an oiled apron which protects them from the dew, a long stick with which to part the leaves and grasses, a wooden bracelet on the left arm, and a badger skin hanging behind from their belt which lets them sit on wet ground. They generally wear a conical hat of birch bark, tied under the chin by a thong, and shoes of tarred pigskin.

Among the Chinese workers and settlers who live in the country the ginseng hunters are always known by their outfit as well as by their peculiar gaze, always lowered to the ground and wandering. Their existence, full of privations and dangers in wild, remote places, gives their mentality a tendency toward asceticism and abnegation. They have left the world, its vanities, joys, and pains. They understand neither our aspira-

* This section is a conflation of passages from three books by Nikolai Apollonovich Baikov (1872–1958), a Russian émigré explorer, traveler, and writer: *V debriakh Manchzhurii* (In the Wilds of Manchuria), Harbin, 1934; *Po belu svetu* (Through the World: Military and Emigrant Stories), Harbin, 1937; and *Taiga shumit* (The Taiga Rustles), Harbin, 1938.

tions nor our conception of life. They are men who have transformed themselves into special beings, gifted with the intelligence and cunning of the Chinese, with a wolf's scent, a falcon's sight, a hare's hearing, and a tiger's quickness.

Man and animal meet in this being, but the animal has in no way stifled the man. In his soul are kept and cultured the poetic feelings of a lover of nature. His entire world is summed up in the taiga. There he passes all his wandering existence, struggling against nature and seeking out the plant which is his living. A true son of the Orient, he believes in fate and predestination, he is superstitious to the marrow of his bones, he carries without complaint his cross of loneliness and privations, without even dreaming of improving the conditions of his unhappy life.

Every year, at the beginning of June, the ginseng hunters go off into the depths of the taiga. They go each their separate ways, rarely in pairs, not carrying arms, strong only in their prayers and the firm belief that the forest and mountain spirits will come to their aid in their undertaking. The patience and resistance of these people are astounding. Dressed in rags, exhausted and undernourished, they wander about the forest with no roads or paths. During their rounds they leave conventional signs, called *kao chu kua,* by breaking branches, making cuts in tree bark, fastening moss or dried grasses to the forks of branches, so that another ginseng hunter will not waste his time going over the same places. Sometimes these poor men die of hunger; often they fall victim to the great beasts of the taiga, tigers, panthers, or bears.

These obstacles and dangers do not lessen the courage and perseverance of the ginseng hunters. The more they must confront perils and privations, the more the mountains are inhospitable, the more the taiga is deep and somber, the more frequent are the animal tracks, then all the more are these men convinced that their efforts will meet with success, for they believe that all these dangers exist only to frighten away cowards, to turn them away from the places where the ginseng grows. In the minds of the Chinese, only a pure and virtuous man can find the root of life. The vicious and immoral man would never know how to succeed there, for the plant disappears at his approach and the root sinks deep into the earth; the mountains begin to totter and the forest to tremble; from the undergrowth springs the terrible ruler of the taiga, ginseng's guardian, the tiger, and he devours the misguided adventurer.

When he finds a plant, the hunter throws aside his stick, covers his eyes with his hand, prostrates himself on the ground and says a prayer to the divinity, which goes about as follows: "Oh Great Spirit! Do not leave me! I have come here with a pure heart and soul, after freeing myself from sins and evil thoughts. Do not leave me!" The prayer said, the hunter may at last glance at the plant he has discovered. He studies the place of discovery with care. The lay of the land, the kind of soil, neighboring plants—everything is taken into consideration and entered in a special notebook. He also needs to observe the place's situation with regard to sun and wind.

Then, after assuring himself that no one has followed and is watching him, the hunter examines the plant itself. If it is solitary, its seeds not having given birth to any nearby plants, he carefully digs away the earth to expose the root for study. By this he determines its value, and if he finds it still too small, he lets it live two or three more years, according to its size; then he puts everything back in place and waters the plant to repay it for the trouble he has caused it. If the plant is in flower, or if its seeds are ripe, it is left until the seeds fall to the ground, in the hope that new seedlings will come up. Often too, the hunter gathers all the roots he finds to replant them where he cultivates ginseng. Whenever he doesn't uproot a plant he has found, he surrounds it with little stakes stuck in the ground, to show that it is reserved. No other hunter will touch it, for in this instance the tradition of the taiga is stronger than personal interest and man's bad instincts.

If the plant is thought worth digging up, that operation is done with the help of special small spades made of bone, called *pan tsui tiang tsi,* six to eight inches long; the hunters carry them on their belt beside the pliable knife which they call *pan tsui tchen tsa*. The work must be done with extreme care, so as not to destroy or damage the long root hairs which descend from the body of the root deep into the earth.

To find again the place where he has left a ginseng root to grow, the hunter marks it with a sign that he alone will be able to recognize. He will make on a nearby tree, for example, a cut with as many notches as there are steps to the plant. The following year he will come by the same place and dig up the plant if it is ready; if not, he will wait a year or two more. If a root is to be transplanted and cultivated, he lifts it, with its surrounding soil, in autumn, when the plant has lost its leaves.

The gathered roots are usually put in a basket of birch bark, after being carefully wrapped in thin paper. They have first had all dirt and useless flakes removed from them; then they were dried and sprinkled with pepper to keep away insects. The upper part of the plant, stem and leaves, are not simply thrown away, but for superstitious reasons are burned. Any seeds are kept for replanting. The berry around the seed is poisonous: taken even in small quantities it produces inflammation of the mucus membranes and vomiting.

Progressive settlement has made the ginseng scarce even in places where it was often found. The result is that the number of ginseng hunters, which was estimated thirty years ago (*c*. 1900) to be 84,000 men in the Ussuri territory and in Manchuria, is now scarcely more than 10,000. Now in these regions only about a thousand roots of wild ginseng are gathered annually, to the value of about a million dollars. Of this amount, three-quarters comes from Manchuria, only a quarter from the Ussuri.

During his explorations across the taiga, the ginseng hunter has nowhere to lay his head. He spends the night wherever evening finds him. If it rains or storms, he takes shelter in a cave or under a rock, or if he is on flat ground he makes a shelter of cedar bark. But he passes most of his nights under the stars, sleeping near a fire on the old badger skin, lying against the trunk of an ancient pine.

Their hunter's trade makes ginseng hunters hardly any

richer, and they remain to the end of their half-wild lives poor vagabonds cynically exploited by the collectors, retailers, and commercial houses. It can be said without exaggeration that every wild ginseng root is watered by the sweat and blood of these nomadic trappers of the taiga. How many silent dramas have been played out in the thickness of the Manchurian forests, all to possess the precious plant.

As soon as the cold, dry autumn wind comes out of the northwest and green things, touched by the earliest frosts, begin to take on their rainbow colors, the hunt for ginseng is cut short. The lucky possessor of a root hurries to quit the taiga for some human settlement. The dangers of the virgin forest are now behind him, but there are other dangers to brave, perhaps greater ones. In a narrow gorge, or on a path along the rocky banks of a river, a bandit waits, a rifle in his hands. Like lightning, the shot's flame pierces the somber depths of the thickets, and its echo resounds along the rocks: the ginseng hunter pitches forward, arms stretched out, his body falls heavily to the ground. The bandit leaps on his victim, frisks him with a practiced hand, opens the birch-bark basket and takes its contents. Then, kicking the body into the raging waters of the river, he runs away into the depths of the forest. The silent taiga will never give up its secret. Only the wind disturbs the topmost heights of the ancient pines, singing its monotonous song.

Several years ago (that is, around the beginning of this century), new kinds of ginseng hunters appeared. They are Chinese workers sent in groups into the taiga by commercial houses and rich merchants. They go over a given region, forming a chain fairly closely linked, which lets them find any ginseng roots lying in their path. The results of this way of hunting are not particularly good, the workers not having the necessary knowledge and experience. But manpower is extremely cheap in China, so the bosses manage to extract a lucrative return from the business.

In his book *Description of the Chinese Empire,* Iakinf writes of the Imperial ginseng harvest in the last years of the

Empire. The harvest is the exclusive province of the Court, which regulates it by special ordinances. Tickets of permission are issued to those who will go on the hunt, 1,752 tickets in Chen-tsin province, 465 in Kirin, 196 in Ninguta, 32 in Bodune, 27 in Achikhe, 33 in Sangsin. Nine thousand hunters go every year into the mountains, and the district governor who has presented the tickets is entitled to a recompense. Anyone guilty of not respecting the rules governing ticket issuance and the harvest is liable to very severe punishment. A special corps of functionaries oversees the gathering; it is dependent on the Imperial Administration. The harvest over, the hunters pass under the Great Wall, escorted by soldiers, and they must there pay a special tax depending on how many roots they have found. All the harvest is brought to the offices of the Imperial Administration which pays to the hunter, as compensation for his traveling and other expenses, five *liangs* (1 *liang* = about 1⅕ ounces) of silver for each *liang* of ginseng. The roots are then closely examined. If any cultivated root is found, there is an inquiry to find out who gave it in and where it comes from, and the guilty party is turned over to the courts. The Imperial Administration divides the ginseng, according to quality, into five categories. They keep at the palace the largest roots of the four first categories; those of the fifth category, as well as broken or damp roots, are in turn divided into three and a half categories and put on the market. One *liang* of fourth-category root is worth 400 *liangs* of silver, of the fifth category 300 *liangs* of silver, broken roots 150 *liangs,* and the smallest roots 100 *liangs*.

The professional hunter would usually sell his harvest to a collector, the *tsai dun,* for a very low price, and deposit his savings in a bank (sometimes he buries them in a hidden corner of the taiga). Every succeeding year he begins again his arduous search, until the day when he falls victim to a two- or four-legged beast.

On nearly all the paths that crisscross the taiga, and especially at the highest point of mountain passes, can be seen little oratories built of unhewn stone or wood. Inside is usually the image of a god (*kua*). These shrines are the work of the Chinese ginseng hunters. From the branches of the trees around they hang pieces of red cotton fabric bearing inscriptions in black Chinese ink. Sometimes the inscriptions are put on little planks fixed to the trees. Usually they read, "To the Lord, the Great Spirit of mountains and woods, give to him who asks of you, do not refuse him. My joy flashes like the scales of a fish, like the feathers of a golden pheasant, when it meets the invisible." On a flat stone found at the entrance to the oratory, all the passersby light perfumed candles, then kneel before the divinity who protects these wild places. The shrines are called *miao* in Chinese; they call them *miao lin* if they are found in mountain passes and *miao ke* if they are beside running water.

In one of these shrines, built at the pass of Lianza-lin, which links the river valleys Mai-ke and Lian-tsu ke, under the altar holding the image of the god, there used to live snakes of the species *Ancystrodon*. The hunters of the region considered them sacred and divinely protected. There were about a dozen of them, and they could often be seen at noon sunning themselves on the altar stones. They were so used to people that you could take them in your hands with no fear of being bitten. According to an old ginseng hunter, when he arrived here as a young man the snakes lived inside the shrine in even greater number. The man said the shrine was built a couple of centuries ago by a ginseng hunter in honor of the "lord of woods and mountains," a tiger who lived at that time in these parts, and to give thanks for an especially precious root he had found nearby. Then in 1909 the Tungus replaced the stone shrine with a wooden construction, built by a Chinese carpenter from the Fried forestry concession, which also furnished the lumber. The new shrine was painted with crimson oil. The snakes continued to live there peacefully until a forest fire in 1913 destroyed their shrine.

Having renounced the world, placing themselves under the gods' protection, the ginseng hunters are especially honored by the natives of the taiga. The Tungus tribes sometimes look after them. Some among them enjoy a great veneration and have considerable influence. Around 1910 there lived near Mount Tikolaza, in a *fansa* bearing that name, an old man of eighty-five years, whom the hunters, the Tungus, and the farmers of the neighborhood called Ko-sin (meaning "spark"). Very likely the name had been given to him because of the eminence of his character. This man was known throughout eastern Manchuria, from the banks of the Sungari to the Korean border and in the Ussuri territory. They say he was very rich, and that his money was buried in several places in the taiga; that he was a sorcerer, able at will to turn a man into an animal; that he could make himself invisible or change into any object whatever. The simple children of the taiga believed that all the animals of the forest obeyed and served him. His extraordinarily penetrating gaze gave forth a hypnotic power and worked no doubt by autosuggestion. He was tall and of robust physique, and presented the general appearance of a young man; the wrinkles of his face alone bore witness to his advanced age. The region around Mounts Tikolaza and Balalaza used to be famous for the abundance of its ginseng, and old Ko-sin, year in and year out, would collect two or three roots to sell to the merchants of the city of Kaiga.

Nowadays you meet fewer and fewer men like this venerable one. They disappear along with all the other inhabitants of the taiga, under the pressure of greedy civilization. They have become anachronisms in the midst of the universal leveling of modern life. Trappers of all sorts, hunters, scouts, and ginseng hunters too, are all giving way little by little to peaceable farmers, who are changing the wild forests of high trees into cultivated fields, uniform and monotonous, though filled with rich harvests. Everything has its season, of course; yet it rends the heart to think of the inevitable fate that dooms these primeval forests, with their mysterious beauty and inexplicable attraction.

One day in July 1910, in one of the deep ravines of Mount Tikolaza, old Ko-sin, wandering about with me, found a very beautiful ginseng root. For weeks in search of the plant we had crossed and crossed again the steep wooded valley of the Lian-tsu ke River. The old man, relying on his experience, had been leading me around this ravine for several days, where indications known only to him predicted a fortunate discovery for us. And in fact after long searching we came to the base of a high mass of granite, from whose top ancient cedars cut their silhouettes against the blue sky. There at the base, among heavy thickets of bracken, wood sorrel, and actinidia,* rose up the thin stem of a ginseng plant. Only Ko-sin's expert eye had been able to distinguish it in the middle of the dense greenery.

On seeing the plant, the old man went up close, knelt, and prostrated himself before it. Then, having carefully inspected the ground around it, he cleared away the grasses and undergrowth surrounding the plant, then uprooted it with the aid of his little bone spades. The length of the root, including the root hairs, was no more than ten inches. It had four leaves, each with five sections. The stem was about fourteen inches long. Later in his *fansa* the man freed the root from the sand and dirt which remained attached to it, removed its stem, laid it on a bed of wadding, wrapped the whole with thin paper, and arranged it in his birch-bark basket. The basket already contained two roots, less beautiful ones, one found five kilometers farther to the north on the rocks of Mount Balalaza, the other, like ours, on Mount Tikolaza. The next day, as I was leaving to return to my house at Kang-dao ke-tse station, Ko-sin gave me as a remembrance the root we had found together. He absolutely refused to accept its price, and asked me only to keep it for good luck. What happened to it afterward is not without interest.

I kept the root until 1914 and never used any of it during that time, except on one occasion. I had a little monkey, an Indian marmot. He lived in a cage in my study, the same room where I kept the ginseng root in a box in a drawer

* A small genus of Asiatic woody vines.

of my desk. One day I went into my study and saw the monkey perched on top of a bookshelf, making gestures at me. He held the root in his hands; the desk drawer was open, and the box was on the floor. I had a lot of trouble catching him and making him give up the root. He had already bitten off a small piece, and had broken a few rootlets. That evening, when the monkey was asleep, I put the ginseng back in its box in the drawer; the next day he found it out again and took it with him to sit above the stove. When I got it away from him again, I took it to the dining room and hid it in the buffet. A few days later the monkey discovered it and carried it to his cage, where he hid it under his blanket.

To find out the interest the ginseng had for my monkey, I tried offering him other roots which looked about the same, but he would recognize the right one every time, snatch it, and carry it back to his cage. He would hold it in his hands, lick it, caress it with his hand, or clutch it to his chest, as if it were a baby. At that time the animal had been showing signs of tuberculosis and two suppurating sores had opened on his tail, with swelling around the infected parts. I let him have the ginseng; he ate a few rootlets; then the swelling began to go down, the pus stopped forming, and a month later the sores were covered with a new, healthy skin. The monkey recovered, put on some weight, and seemed in excellent health. Whether this cure happened by chance or not I don't know, but I can vouch for the facts I witnessed.

Leaving for the front in 1914, I left the root with a friend in Kiev. In 1916 it was exhibited in a store window in the center of town. Chinese would often enter the shop to ask the price of the root, and leave disappointed to learn that it was not for sale. In September 1916, a richly dressed Chinese asked the proprietor please to tell him the owner of the root. That December a Chinese, very likely the same one, came out to find me on the Carpathian front and proposed to buy the root for a thousand rubles. He even offered me fifteen hundred, but I refused both offers categorically. He insisted, came back to see me several times, always without success, and finally left with a warning that I would be sorry for my stubbornness. In January the store owner wrote me that the root had disappeared in the most mysterious manner: he suspected it had been stolen by an employee and sold to a Chinese, but he had no proof and could not accuse anyone. He told me afterward that he had experienced an incomprehensible anguish, which at times reached the stage of hallucinations, all the time the root was on exhibit in his store, that it positively drew him. It was only after its disappearance that he experienced some relief, even though he felt morally responsible for its theft.

When he gave me the root, the old hunter had said to keep it always by me, in my bedroom, and to keep it in a box always wrapped with tin foil. Besides, he had recommended using it only in good earnest and when extremely necessary. I never had the opportunity to test its effect on myself. It was bittersweet and rather hot to the taste. The store owner

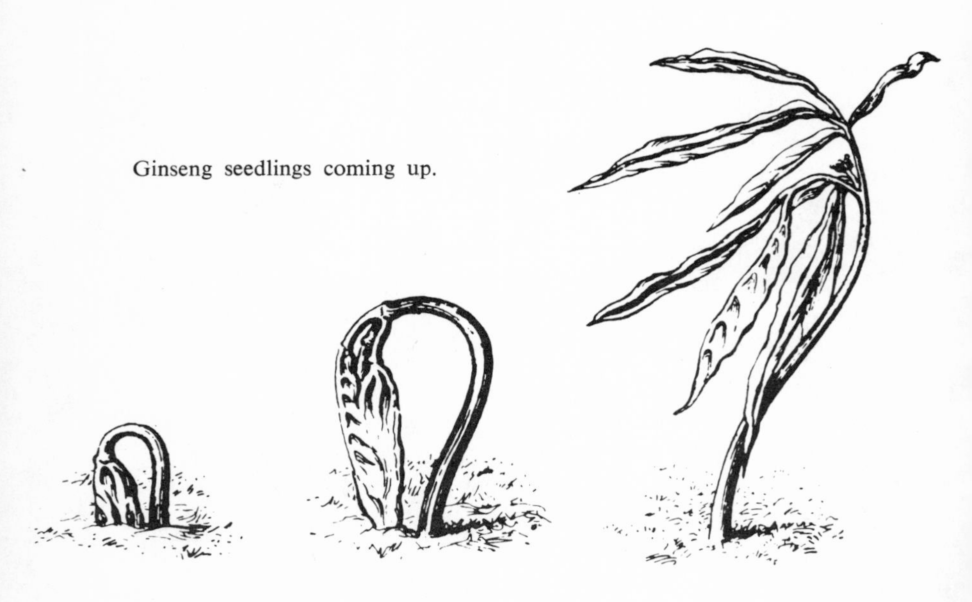

Ginseng seedlings coming up.

assured me that in humid weather it would give off a barely visible phosphorescent glow and a certain spicy odor. I never had occasion to see the phosphorescence, but certainly remember the peculiar smell.

GINSENG CULTURE

Ginseng is planted from freshly gathered seeds; otherwise they rapidly lose their vital force. Before planting they must be kept three weeks in a humid place or in damp sand, at a temperature of 8°C. The cultivator chooses with great care the site of his plantation, generally in a forest of mixed trees where cedars are growing, in a northern exposure.

Where he will set up his beds, he digs a trench a meter or two deep, that he fills with the best rich earth, previously kneaded by hand and sifted twice. When the beds are ready he plants the seeds, six inches down, and lays a light covering of dried leaves and needles over them. To protect them from the wind, he plants all around grasses and shrubs with big leaves, or ferns, or perhaps he will build windbreaks made of birch bark. The seed will generally not sprout until the second year. But if the shoot has not appeared by the second year, you must not lose patience, but wait still another year: the seed is not dead but has not yet found the necessary conditions for growth. The sun's rays have a bad effect on the plants, so hoods of cedar or birch bark are usually set up above them, constructed so that the sunlight will strike the plants only from seven to nine o'clock in the morning, and from five to seven in the evening.

The planter waters the beds with sprinklers specially made with a fine spray, so as not to damage the tender young shoots. Watering is usually done in the evening, before sunset. The soil must be dampened up to a certain degree, but not soaked, for the roots will rot in excessively wet ground. Some advise planting wood sorrel around ginseng, believing the nearness of the sorrel would have a favorable effect on ginseng's growth. A cultivated ginseng root is never as heavy and large as the root of the wild plant; the first rarely weighs more than 250 grams, while the second may well weigh a pound.

Some planters employ another procedure, which is to transplant wild ginseng seedlings into a special bed. When the plants lose their leaves in autumn, they are dug up with all the soil surrounding the roots, so that no harm is caused even to the finest rootlets. The soil of the new bed should be as close as possible in composition to that where the wild plants grew. Cultivated ginseng is usually uprooted and sold when it is six or seven years old. A transplanted wild root is more appreciated than a cultivated root but sells in any case for far less than wild ginseng. The Chinese say that it will lose some of its qualities the first year after transplanting. So the hunters always prefer to leave wild ginseng in place to reach its full growth, especially since it is generally not they who cultivate the root. They will transplant only when there is no hope of keeping the plant in the place where they found it.

The ginseng planters are for the most part the sedentary inhabitants of the taiga, small-game hunters and trappers or gold prospectors who have much leisure time in summer. With wild ginseng becoming ever rarer, cultivation has greatly developed in recent years. Now you see plantations frequently in many regions of the taiga, far from the nearest dwelling or means of communication. Usually they contain from four to six beds, each twenty-five feet long and holding ten to twenty plants. Sometimes there is only one bed, no more than ten feet long, containing five or six specimens. It is hard to spot ginseng plantations in the taiga's denseness, for they are usually placed in almost inaccessible places and hidden as much as possible from prying eyes. No path will lead to them, and the planter will go there each time by a different route. To protect the plants against the big animals—boars, bears, and wapiti deer—the planter will surround the beds with fences of felled trees. The proprietor of a large plantation will generally live nearby, in a cabin built of uncut stones and cedar bark.

Cultivated ginseng roots arrive in the market cleaned of their dried-up outer skin, rootlets and beard, while the wild roots are kept just the way they come from the ground. Ginseng plantations are most numerous and the roots are of highest quality in the south of Kirin province, with its steep, wooded river valleys. In the Ussuri basin ginseng is grown on the north slopes of Mount Khekhtsira, in the high valley of the Iman River, and in the Da-tiang lin Mountains. Cultivated ginseng production cannot now be given in exact figures, but it would be fair to guess that annual production is from five to six thousand kilos. In the province nearest the sea there used to be large plantations on the land of the settler Yankovsky, but they disappeared during the civil war. In northern Korea ginseng cultivation was undertaken by the Japanese and Koreans in the high valleys of the Tumyang gan and Yalu Rivers, but connoisseurs generally say that Korean roots are not worth those of Kirin. At the present time the business has no special taxes levied on it, which makes it difficult to get correct production figures.

Every planter sets up an oratory nearby, usually against the trunk of an old cedar or a great fir. He cuts a gash in the tree, waist high and about ten inches deep, then chops away a part of the trunk to make a little platform, on which goes a container of sand for the perfumed candles. Higher up on the trunk he hangs a picture of the protecting god of his plantation, or a picture of the tiger, lord of the forest. Every day after sunset the planter kneels before his little temple, lights the scented candles, and asks the Great Spirit to protect his precious plants from attack and harm. The Tungus and the hunters, whenever they come upon one of these oratories in the forest, think it their duty to say a prayer and to make the offering of a small piece of cloth which they hang from the nearby branches.

No dweller of the taiga will touch a ginseng bed; it is as

sacred as the wild plant. Very rarely will a solitary thief dare to steal a root, for he sets his own fate thereby, and will never escape the terrible retribution of the taiga: sooner or later he is found dead in his cabin, even if it is far away from the scene of his crime. The avenger need not always be the owner of the stolen plant; he might be one of those who knew of the theft, a crime the taiga's law punishes by death. If a ginseng hunter or planter is murdered, all the men of the taiga will take vengeance. Sometimes the Tungus take up the victim's cause and assume the role of executioners.

So we can see that the attraction of the miraculous root extends to all those in direct contact with it. The plant is a kind of stimulant of justice and good, a symbol of the balance between natural, creative forces. The Chinese idea is that the root itself contains a part of the Great Spirit: ginseng is the seed of life, the source of movement, invisible light, and universal energy, inspired, possessing the supernatural force which distinguishes divinity. It can change itself into an animal, a man, another plant, or any other object. Thus no unworthy person can ever find it. If someone in the forest sees an animal, a bird, or even a stone, and the next moment sees them no more, he is sure he has seen a transformed ginseng plant. He must pray then, repent his sins, and the following year he may return to the same place to look for the root. If someone has committed a crime and has not sincerely repented it, the ginseng becomes a tiger and devours the sinner. In his next life he becomes a lower animal, then passes through various incarnations which, by purifying him, allow him to return through higher stages and become a man again.

According to a legend that is often told, the origin of ginseng is as follows: in a very ancient time, the plant used to grow in southern China, and no one knew of its existence. But then the great sage Lao-tse found it and discovered its powerful curative virtues. He told the people of his discovery and explained to them how to recognize the plant. But ginseng disappeared from the south, then reappeared in the north, in the Tchi-li Mountains. The great Lao Khan-van, a learned and thoughtful prince, was able to find the plant again by means of scholarly research. But ginseng, in order to escape from mankind and its vanities, fled away further to the north, into the inaccessible Ch'ang-pai shan Mountains and the virgin woods of Chou-kai (Kirin province) and the Sikhote-Alin Mountains. Centuries passed, but the legend of ginseng lived always in men's hearts. At last one day the three brothers Van-go, Ka-so van, and Liu-lu came from the central part of China to search for the marvelous plant. They lost their way in the deep forests of Chou-kai and perished there. Their souls have ever since been incarnate in birds' bodies, and fly across the taiga, calling to one another. When a traveler in the taiga hears the call of these birds, he never follows the sound, but heads in the opposite direction; otherwise he may be certain of his fate: he will become lost and die, like the three brothers. The bird is a small owl, of the species *Scops,* often heard during the warm nights of summer.

To escape the pursuit of man, ginseng has begotten numerous plants closely resembling it, which the hunters call *pan-tsui.* Finding true ginseng is therefore very difficult. The closer a *pan-tsui* is planted to a ginseng root, the more the latter will resemble a human body, and its potency and price will be accordingly greater. Cultivated ginseng is also sometimes called *pan-tsui.*

In the forests which cover the great river valley of the Mu-tan kiang, the ginseng hunters told me another legend of the plant's origin. According to them, the rulers of the Ch'ang-pai shan Mountains, on the Korean frontier, used to be two rival clans, one called Si-lian tse and the other Lian-se erh. They were continually at war with each other. One of the members of the first clan, the famous warrior Ginseng, was a fearless and worthy soldier, protector of the poor, the weak, the oppressed, the afflicted. He had inherited these good qualities from his ancestors, themselves descended from the king of beasts, the strong and wise tiger. The other family did not have the same virtues, but was distinguished only by its beauty and cruelty. Son-chi ko, a member of this clan, had become a *hunghutze* (bandit), and persecuted and plundered the poor people. Ginseng, roused to indignation by the excesses committed by Son-chi ko, attacked him, made him his prisoner, put him in irons, and threw him in a dungeon. He would have died there if the graceful Liu-la, Ginseng's sister, had not become smitten with his beauty: she opened his prison and fled with him into the mountains. Ginseng quickly pursued them, and caught up with them in the wild gorge of Siao-sui fing. Seeing her brother approaching, Liu-la hid herself behind a rock. The two enemies began their struggle. Son-chi ko was strong, but Ginseng had the power and agility of the tiger; he struck a mortal blow at his enemy's heart. Seeing this, Liu-la screamed in terror. Ginseng turned around to her, but the movement was fatal to him. Gathering his last strength, Son-chi ko stabbed him through the heart. For a long time the beautiful Liu-la mourned her brother and lover; in the end she became as dried up as a dead flower. Where her tears fell there grew a plant unknown up to that time, ginseng, the man-root, source of life.

There is another legend which says that ginseng was born from the lightning. High up in the heavens repose the powerful forces which send to earth rain, snow, hail, and lightning: two of the opposing elements of nature, water and fire. These two life elements, like good and evil, light and darkness, movement and repose, are always hostile to one another; it is this elemental antipathy, this struggle and constant disturbance which creates life and the universal harmony which reconciles the opposites. If lightning strikes the pure and limpid water of a mountain spring, the spring disappears under ground, and ginseng will grow in its place, the plant which contains the power of heavenly fire, inexhaustible energy of the universe. That is why the Chinese sometimes call ginseng "the root of lightning" (*chang-diang shen*).

In the forests of the former Imperial Preserve, where much ginseng used to be found, an old trapper who had served in the banners of the Son of Heaven told me a typical story of the mysterious bird Kongultotchou, a guardian of the fabulous plant. In ancient times there lived two brothers, Li-u and Kongultotchou. Searching for ginseng, they went deep into the forests of the Lao-e lin Mountains. For a long time they wandered in the taiga, and in the end Kongultotchou, the younger brother, lost his way and perished. His brother searched for him for several years, calling his name in every corner of the forest. The Mountain Spirit was moved by the grief of Li-u and took pity on him, turning him into a bird, which ever since has flown from tree to tree in the taiga, calling the brother's name. If a traveler hears this nearly human voice and follows it, he will never come back: the voice will lead him into woods so dense that he will not be able to get out. If any novice ginseng hunter lets himself be led on by the voice, it will take him into the clutches of the tiger, the guardian of ginseng.

The Chinese say that the bird still exists today. No one knows its species. It is about as big as a jackdaw and has variegated plumage. It keeps to the tops of the tallest trees and never descends to earth. Its characteristic cry of four notes seems to come from a flute and can be heard from a great way off. But one only hears it in spring, when the May lilies flower. It is very difficult to approach it with rifle in hand, for the bird is fearful of man and will fly away, going from treetop to treetop, repeating its call. The old inhabitants of the taiga are convinced that the bird watches over the ginseng and leads astray the hunters, making them wander vainly through the forests. Its cry is generally said to herald calamity or defeat.

Every particularly precious ginseng root, just as a diamond of the first water, has a more or less plausible history. Stories begin which then are recounted for hundreds of miles around. Thus, for example, we hear that around the end of the last century a mandarin from Ninguta had a ginseng root which acted on people so strongly as to cause them abscesses and inflammations, even through the walls of the box where he kept it. At night it gave off a greenish glow which came through the wooden planks of the box. The mandarin finally had to give over the root to the governor of Kirin, who in turn made a present of it to the Son of Heaven.*

Besides their curative properties, most of the first-rate roots also function as talismans, bringing good luck to the owners; yet there are also those roots which bring misfortune, even while keeping their therapeutic virtues. The Chinese believe that ginseng can even bring a dead man back to life, if it is used in time by a knowledgeable person.

GINSENG IN ORIENTAL MEDICINE

We should first remark that the idea of curing illnesses and serious diseases is not unique to man. We can see that mammals and even birds, because of the powerful instinct for self-preservation, turn sometimes to a traditional remedy to cure them of some ailment or other. Dogs and cats often eat grass to purge themselves. Some birds consume sand and little pebbles to recover proper digestion. So the idea of therapy exists in nature, and man, in perfecting himself, has also perfected his curative methods.

In the Middle Ages, when European medicine was still in its infancy, and doctors and scientists still believed in the miraculous power of an elixir of life, able even to revive the dead, Chinese medicine was by comparison infinitely more advanced, and likewise had its elixir of life in the ginseng plant. At that time Chinese healers had already, based on long and minute experiments, established scientific methods of therapy. The root of life was already considered as one of the most efficacious remedies.

There is no doubt at all that ginseng contains essential curative virtues. Along with the new horns of the wapiti deer, which are called *panty,* ginseng plays a very important part in Oriental medicine. It is given in many ways, mainly, when mixed with other preparations, in the form of pills, but

* Son of Heaven (*t'ien tzu*) as used here is one of the commonest designations for "emperor."

powder, decoctions, infusions, extracts, and unguents are also made from it. The powder is made from the dried root, grated very fine; it is used in making pills, along with other ingredients, such as *panty,* a decoction of bear bones, the gall of the same animal, milk-vetch root, and several marine plants containing iodine. The paste from which the pills are made is kneaded with refined nut oil.

The infusion is prepared in the following way: you clean the root with a brush, place it in an earthenware pan, and boil it in lightly sugared water, then put it for a while in steam, finally let it dry out in warm, dry air. After these operations the root assumes a yellow-orange color and becomes transparent, like amber; the taste is spicy and bittersweet. Now put the root in a bottle of very strong spirits, and let it infuse in a warm place until the alcohol takes on a saffron color. Remove the root from the bottle, but do not throw it away.

Ginseng extract is made in a hermetically sealed container, which is plunged into boiling water and kept there until several drops of an almost black liquid—the essence of the root—are formed at the bottom of the container. For decoctions, place the root in boiling water in an enameled earthenware pan and boil it until completely soft; remove and dry. These roots are often then sold as waste products, though still at a rather high price. Keep the decoction in a glass bottle; it is brown in color and has a bitter taste. Unguents are prepared in many different ways, according to their intended use. Usually a preparation of fresh turtle fat is used, along with musk of the musk deer and owl brains, all mixed with ginseng powder in strictly determined proportions.

Before taking any remedies containing ginseng, it is advisable to put oneself under a strict regimen. The first condition is physical exercise in the open air, as well as sexual continence and moderation in all things. Stimulating beverages are absolutely forbidden: coffee, tea, vinegar, and spirits. During the warm season, and at any time that heart palpitations develop, cease the medication or diminish the dose.

Take a normal quantity in winter. The strongest dose should be taken at the beginning of spring. Being ignorant of all these rules, Westerners take ginseng without observing them and this, say the Chinese, is the reason the remedy doesn't produce much effect. One should not take a preparation of pure ginseng, an imprudence which may lead to bleeding from the nose or gums, or even general constitutional decay. The pills should be taken in the morning before breakfast or in the evening before retiring. The daily dose is from a minimum of three pills to a maximum of fifteen. A small liqueur glass of the alcoholic infusion may be taken before each meal.

Remedies based on ginseng are sold in all Chinese pharmacies. The price is not particularly high, but naturally varies according to the quality of the roots used. The remedies' effectiveness depends on the pharmacist's honesty. No rich Chinese will fail to add to his daughter's trousseau some *panty,* or to give to his son, the day he marries him off, a ginseng root of high quality. This is an ancient Chinese custom, probably still observed today.

Ginseng is a universal remedy curing numerous diseases. It is used against anemia, cachexia,* scrofula, gastrointestinal catarrh, general debility, any malfunction of the lungs, kidneys, liver, heart, or genital organs. Against nervous diseases, ginseng is used combined with wild honey, bromine, and a seminal gland extract of the wapiti deer. To cure tuberculosis, extracts and decoctions of ginseng are employed, at the same time as a preparation composed of *panty,* and bear fat. This medication will not succeed unless the patient follows a strict diet and is able to breathe pure air, free of dust.

For several years now, ginseng has been used as a treatment for syphilis. The suitable preparations here are decoctions and infusions, but along with this medication the patient is given other remedies made of herbs mixed with bear gall. Syphilis may perhaps be completely cured by ginseng; it is certain that its symptoms cease rapidly. Malignant fever and malaria yield

* General physical wasting or malnutrition caused by chronic disease.

completely to the use of certain bitter drops* taken with a spoonful of ginseng infusion; sunflowers and their seeds are among the component parts of this mixture. Chronic gastro-intestinal catarrh can be very rapidly cured when the patient undergoes a strict diet, drinks a glass of black radish juice morning and evening, and a glass of ginseng infusion before meals. At the end of the period of treatment, he should take a small glass of elderberry infusion after meals. In general ginseng is given in many preparations, combined with other medication, and in very varied doses.

Tibetan medicine, which gave birth to Chinese, also grants a primordial importance to ginseng and includes it in many remedies. In the regions of the Orient where Buddhism is practiced, the lamas are the rulers, and many among them take on the functions of healers; moreover, medical science is one of the branches of knowledge they have acquired in their monasteries. But one meets few lamas who have studied medicine deeply. Instead there are many, not knowing the principles of medical art, who care for the sick with traditional recipes or according to the *tarni,* the vast collection of Buddhist and lamaist literature dealing with spiritualism, hypnotism, interpretation of dreams, and incantations. In a lower category there are healing lamas so ignorant that they scarcely know the *tarni* at all and mainly make use in their practice of formulas and rituals.

In Buddhist doctrine, the lamas are considered the successors of Buddha and guardians of the Master's precepts. They also preserve the wisdom and soul of Oriental medical science. There is an abundant medical literature in Tibetan which is concerned with all the areas of life. Some of the works are so rare that even the richest monasteries do not have them. It is a sum of medical knowledge going back at least twenty centuries which has always been *terra incognita* for Westerners. It was set forth in a manual of practical medicine and surgery entitled *Jud Chi.* The science established precise ideas

* Probably quinine, a specific drug for malaria and malignant fever; the use of ginseng here would seem to be superfluous.

about the well and the sick body, diagnoses of the illnesses it may contract, about food, drink, and the kind of life to lead, about cures, remedies, and the milieu in which men live. These ideas are the result of a profound study of human life from conception until the last moment of earthly existence.

The principles of Tibetan medical science originated in India in remotest antiquity, but they were mainly developed and perfected in Tibet. The names of the earliest pioneers of this science, as those of the originators of so much of our knowledge, are lost in the night of ages. Medicine had then a religious and legendary character; the first Hindu physicians were gods and dwellers in Heaven.

The most ancient medical work, composed even before the appearance of Buddha Sakyamuni (Gautama) carries the title *Zaraga Dib Jad*. The later work, *Jud Chi,* appeared in Tibet in Sakyamuni's time. Its title means "The Nectar Heart; the eight branches of the four principles of special therapy." This work is a résumé of all medical science, and the term "special therapy" is explained by the fact that from earliest times therapeutics was considered the aim of medical study.

The book's first chapter begins with an invocation: "Hail to thee, Buddha, chief of physicians." The lamas believe that Sakyamuni himself taught the *Jud Chi,* for their predecessors, who profited from medical learning, gave to Tso Jed Chonu, the author of the work, all the epithets of Buddha. Legend says that he lived in the fourth century B.C. and was the friend of Sakyamuni and the famous Greek physician Herophilus. The original of his book has not been found, but it appears certain that he knew the Vedas, for the two works have many points and passages in common. It was put into its present form later by the famous Tibetan doctor, Yugtog-bé Yondon Gonbo, whose vast work of eighteen chapters is called *Chalog Job Jad*. The eighth chapter encompasses all needful knowledge for a practicing physician in the fields of embryology, anatomy, physiology, pathology, diagnosis, hygiene, pharmacognosy, pharmacology, and surgery. The last ten chapters treat the role of the nervous system when the organism is badly nourished.

At the end of the seventeenth century, the physician Namjal Davana wrote numerous medical works which were approved by the clerical and lay authorities of the Buddhist world. Among other things he wrote a three-part manual called, in translation, *Fundamentals of Medicine,* a commentary on the *Jud Chi* (*Gaprin Muntsel*) and a work called *Rinchin Dombu.* These diverse manuals are now the principal documents of Tibetan medical science. The chief medical school is in the monastery of Kakpuri near Lhasa; there is collected much of the medical knowledge of the contemporary Orient.

Buddhist empiricism is strange and rough, but it is marked with the seal of centuries, having undergone the experience of many generations. In thousands of cases we have witnessed the thankfulness and veneration of the peoples spread over the immensity of Asia, from India to Siberia, from the shores of the Caspian to the Land of the Rising Sun.

DERSU THE TRAPPER *

Dersu was a Gold, a member of a Manchurian tribe—now nearly entirely assimilated—of great hunters, trappers, and ginseng seekers. In the 1920s he led Arseniev, a "white" Russian, on three successive expeditions into the Manchurian taiga, serving as guide, interpreter, and companion.

Next morning before it was light I took a Cossack and started off. It soon grew light, the moon grew pale and feeble, the shadows vanished, and softer tones appeared. The dawn breeze fluttered the treetops and aroused the feathered inhabitants. The sunlight climbed higher up in the sky, and then suddenly the life-giving rays of the sun itself burst out from behind the crest, and at once lit up the whole scene, trees, bushes, and grass, all glistening with dew.

* V. K. Arseniev, *Dersu the Trapper* (Malcolm Burr trans.), New York, 1941, pp. 84–87; 134–136; 150–152 *passim.*

Near the first cabin we did in fact find a small track leading to the side, which brought us to a second, similar cabin, where we found a couple of Chinese, one young, the other an old man, the former a trapper, the latter a hunter for ginseng. The younger was a strongly built fellow of about five-and-twenty, and from his face it was clear that he enjoyed life, was happy and contented with his lot. He was constantly laughing, and playing some prank all the time. The old man was tall, cadaverous, and more like a mummy than a living man. From his heavily lined and wrinkled skin and weather-beaten face and gray hair I guessed he was in his seventies. Both were wearing blue jackets, blue trousers, gaiters and *uly,** but the younger man's clothes were new and cared for, while the old fellow's were old and crumpled. The first wore a straw hat that he had bought somewhere, the other a home-made one of birch bark.

The old man carried himself with great dignity and talked little, but his companion was a regular chatterbox. He told me that in the taiga they had a ginseng plantation and that was where they were then going. I was so interested in what he was telling me that I lost my sense of direction, and without their help I doubt if I could have found my way back to their hut. We walked across the flanks of the hills for an hour, crossed a cliff, and then dropped into a valley. On the way we passed several mountain torrents and deep gullies, with snow still lingering in them, and then at last we reached our destination. It was a northern slope of a mountain, covered with thick woodland.

The reader will be quite wrong if he pictures to himself a ginseng plantation in the form of a garden with regular sown crops. A place where some roots of ginseng have been found is looked upon as suitable, and here they bring all their other roots. The first thing that I saw was screens of cedar bark to protect the precious plant from the scorching rays of the sun, and to keep the soil cool there were beds of ferns planted at

* Moccasins of hide lined with Manchurian *ula* grass (*cf.* p. 4).

the sides, and a small irrigation canal brought water from the brook.

On arrival at the garden the old man fell on his knees, folded his arms with the palms together, pressed them to his brow, and twice bowed low to the ground, all the time muttering something to himself, no doubt prayers. Then he stood up, placed his hands on his head, and then started work. The younger man meanwhile had been hanging some red tags on the trees with inscriptions on them.

There is no other plant in the world round which has gathered so many legends and stories. Under the influence of literature or of the stories of the Chinese, I do not know why, but I myself felt some sort of respect for this ordinary-looking representative of the *Araliaceæ*. I knelt down so as to have a closer look at it. The old man understood this in his own way, that I was praying, and from that moment he was entirely at my service.

Both men set to work. They removed dry branches fallen from the trees, planted a few twigs, and watered them. Noticing that too little water was reaching the nursery, they admitted more. Then they started weeding, not taking out all the weeds, but only some. The kind that annoyed them most was *Eleutherococcus.**

Leaving them to their work, I went for a stroll in the taiga. Afraid of losing my way, I followed down the stream, so as to be able to come back the same way. When I came back to the ginseng garden the men had finished their work and were waiting for me. We arrived at their cabin from the other direction, so had evidently returned by another route.

Few reach the very heart of the taiga. It is too vast. The wayfarer is ever struggling with the force of vegetation. Many secrets does the taiga conceal in her breast, hiding them jealously from prying eyes of man. She seems morose and grim. That is the first impression. But the man who grows to know

* *Eleutherococcus senticosus,* a medicinal herb that grows wild over much of western Asia, is believed to be antipathetic to ginseng, which it resembles slightly.

her better soon becomes accustomed to her, and pines when taken away from the forest if he does not see the forest for long. It is only outwardly that the taiga seems dead; in truth she is full of life.

Dersu and I walked on unhurriedly, watching the birds. In the clumps of undergrowth here and there flitted a brisk little rustic bunting, and I caught an occasional glimpse of the little Ussurian woodpeckers. Most interesting of these was the green one with the golden crest. It hammered away busily at the trees, paying no attention to the approach of men. A few dusky thrushes flew across, some jays flew off, and once we startled a merlin, which flew low and was soon lost among the trees.

Dragonflies appeared over the water. A wagtail gave chase, but the insect was too quick for it.

Suddenly behind me a nutcracker uttered his cry of alarm. Dersu signed me to stop.

"Wait, captain," he said. "Him come here."

And in fact the sound approached. There was no doubt that this timid bird was escorting something through the wood. I was right. In five minutes a man appeared among the thickets. He stopped dead, as though petrified, and his face showed great alarm.

I knew him at once for a ginseng seeker. He was dressed in the usual shirt and breeches of blue *daba* (cotton), skin moccasins, and a birch-bark hat upon his head. In front hung an oiled apron to protect his trousers from the dew and from his belt behind hung a badger skin, so that he could sit on a log without wetting them. From his girdle hung a knife, a piece of bone for digging up ginseng roots, and a bag with flint and steel. In his hands he carried a long staff for scraping away grass and leaves on the ground.

Dersu told him not to be afraid, and he came nearer. He was a man of about fifty-five, already turning gray. His hands and face were burned to a uniform greenish red. He was unarmed.

When the man realized that we meant him no harm, he sat on a log, pulled a rag out of his shirt, and wiped his face.

The old man's expression showed extreme exhaustion.

So this was a hunter for ginseng! In his way he was a sort of hermit, who buried himself in the mountains and entrusted himself to the protection of the spirits of the forest.

In answer to our inquiry, he told us that he had a cabin on the upper waters of the Dinzahé, but in his search for the wonder-working root he sometimes wandered so far from home that it took him weeks to make his way back.

He told us how to find the way to his cabin and invited us to stop there. After a little rest the old fellow bade us farewell, picked up his staff, and went on his lonely way. Long I followed him with my eyes. Once he stopped, picked up a handful of moss, and put it on a tree. Farther on he tied a knot in a twig of a bird cherry. Those are signals to show others who might come that way that he had worked it for ginseng and drawn blank. There is true philosophy in that, to prevent the seekers from walking over the same ground and wasting time. In a few minutes the old man disappeared from view, and we continued on our road.

At noon (of the following day) we came to a dense forest, where we halted for a breather, and I had a look round at the vegetation. Age-old oaks, mighty cedars, black birch, maple, *Aralia,* firs, poplars, hornbeam, spruce, larch, and yew all grew together in picturesque profusion. The forest here had some peculiar feature of its own. Below, under the trees, reigned twilight. Dersu walked slowly, and, as usual, kept his eye attentively on the ground at his feet. Suddenly he stopped and, without taking his eyes off some object, began to remove his knapsack, lay down his rifle and prop, threw down his ax, and lay full length on the ground, and began praying.

I thought he had gone crazy.

"Dersu!" I exclaimed. "What is it?"

"Pantsui!" he cried. "Ginseng!"

Here there was a mass of herbage, but which was the ginseng I did not know. Dersu showed it to me. I saw a small, herbaceous plant about fourteen inches high, with four leaves. Each leaf consisted of five divisions, of which the middle was the longest, the outside ones the shortest. It had already flowered, and the fruit appeared. This was in the form of small rounded cases, arranged like those of umbelliferous plants. The cases had not yet opened or scattered their seed. Dersu cleared the weeds all round it, then picked off all the seedcases and tied them up in a bit of rag. Then he asked me to hold the plant up with my hand, while he dug up the root. He worked extremely carefully, taking every precaution to avoid tearing the fibers. When he had got it out he took it to the brook and started carefully washing off the soil.

I helped him as best I could. Gradually the earth came away and in a few minutes we could examine the root. It was four and a half inches long and forked, that is to say a male. So that was the famous ginseng, whose magic power is sovereign against all ills of the flesh and restores to the aged the vigor of youth! Dersu cut off the plant, and packed it, together with the root, in moss in a roll of bark. Then he muttered some prayer, slipped on his knapsack again, picked up his weapon and prop, and exclaimed, "You lucky, captain!"

On the road I asked the Gold what he was going to do with his ginseng. He said he wanted to sell it and buy cartridges with the money. Then I decided to buy the ginseng myself and offered him a better price than the Chinese would give. When I told him of this decision the result was quite unexpected. Dersu thrust his hand inside his jacket, pulled out the roll, and handed it to me, saying that it was a gift. I declined it, but he insisted. I saw that my refusal offended him, and so accepted. It was only afterward that I learned that it was the custom to repay gifts by gifts of equal value.

THE RED GINSENG DEVIL *

Ferdinand Ossendowski, a Pole, served as President of the Far Eastern Revolutionary Government during the abortive Russian Revolution of 1905. His death sentence was commuted to a few years' imprisonment. After the Bolshevik

* Ferdinand Ossendowski, *Man and Mystery in Asia,* in collaboration with Lewis Stanton Palen, London, 1924, pp. 98–102.

Revolution of 1917 he returned to Poland, where he wrote of his extensive travel and study in the Far East, mainly in eastern Siberia and Mongolia, in the early years of this century.

It would be difficult, well-nigh impossible, for me to forget my expedition north of Vladivostok to make geological studies in search of coal and gold. A wild taiga, this Ussuri forest —a green ocean, a mixture of northern and southern flora. Here, on the farther bank of the Ussurian Bay, I found the silent, solitary ravines of the middle Sikhote-Alin. Forest roads, winding and disappearing, led from *fansa* to *fansa* inhabited by Russian and Chinese hunters.

Often I entered these *fansa,* sometimes received willingly and hospitably, but sometimes the owner of the hut, seeing me approach, left the house and hid in the bushes, and sometimes even a bullet from an invisible rifle sang above my head as a warning to avoid the dwelling of one not fond of human society.

One evening a light shone through the branches. I went in its direction and soon saw a little house made of logs chinked with clay. A stockade of poles with a heavy gate of crudely hewn planks surrounded this *fansa* where I called for the gate to be opened, and my Cossack guide pounded on it with the butt of his rifle. We finally heard some mumblings and dull, incomprehensible gruntings. The door slowly opened and a paper lantern first appeared, followed by the thin, terrified face of a Chinese with big frightened eyes. His pigtail was twisted around his head and a pipe was thrust through the coils.

"Ni liao hao (How do you do)?" my Cossack greeted him in his best Chinese.

The man shook his head and muttered, but we could understand nothing, even though my guide spoke the Manchurian dialect fluently. The Chinese continued to mumble in a dull, toneless voice. Finally he opened his mouth wide, holding the lantern near his face so that we saw his tongue was cut out and his front teeth were broken.

The Cossack soon succeeded in understanding the cripple

and told me that our host was a seeker of ginseng and that once he was attacked in his house here in the forest by *hung-hutzes* (bandits). They ordered him to give them all he had of the precious root and, when he refused to comply with their demands, they began to torture him and finally cut out his tongue, but he did not disclose where he had hidden his precious roots. Explaining this with mumblings and gestures, the Chinese seemed to make clear to us that now after all his maiming he was afraid of nothing and would tell nobody, including ourselves, his secret.

We took up our quarters in his home and tried to be comfortable. We brought fresh grass for a good bed, unsaddled our horses and tied them under a little shed near the *fansa,* carried water from the stream, and began to prepare our supper. The Chinese, with suspicions allayed and relieved by the fact that we asked for nothing and treated him even to tobacco and sugar, brought us a basket of pheasants' eggs and a bunch of sea cabbage.

After supper and tea, which he took with us, he became more communicative. He mumbled more quickly and loudly, making gestures with his hands and looking round into all corners of the room. Finally he disappeared for a moment into some sort of hole and returned with an enigmatic face. When he neared the *kang* (the Chinese flue-heated brick bed) he held something in one hand, covering it with the other. In the light of our candle he placed on the *kang* two big strangely formed brown roots, their shape distinctly resembling that of the human body, with head, torso, feet, and hands. Even long, matted hair grew on the head. The Cossack, an expert in these things, carefully inspected the roots and said afterward with a sad sigh, "In Vladivostok or Khabarovsk one could get twice its weight in gold for this ginseng, as these are particularly valuable, old, healthy roots."

I inferred from his sigh and his regretful, meditative expression that, had I not been there, the dumb Chinese would have to undergo new tortures and would be forced to reveal where he hid his treasures, so sought for in the East.

At midnight, a second ginseng hunter, partner of the tongueless man, came in. He was a giant, with a severe, almost terrible face, with broad shoulders and the powerful neck of a bear. When he moved about the room he shook the whole establishment. He stopped before us and, after scrutinizing us, with his eyes questioned his dumb partner. The answer visibly pleased him, as he put his rifle in one corner, took his ax from his belt and, giving us a side glance, took from his pocket a little leather bag and gave it to his companion, who turned to the light and quickly untied the bag, gloating over the spoil. Evidently it was good, for he mumbled joyfully and clapped his hands like a child. The giant undressed wearily, swallowed some millet gruel and tea and, loudly groaning, flung himself on the *kang*. Soon he was snoring like a pig, while the dumb one had once more disappeared in his hole and remained there a long time. I had the impression that I heard the noise of rolling stones and the dull rattle of iron; but perhaps it was a dream only, as I did not remember when the poor fellow returned.

We were up at dawn and had our tea with dry bread and biscuits. The giant, still grunting and terribly tired, proved to be talkative and sociable. He spoke Russian fairly well, as he had been a "boy" in Vladivostok for several years. I must say that I thought that he must have done considerable damage, as I pictured to myself this servant with the body of an elephant and the neck of a bear serving dinner, polishing Baccarat glassware or ironing fine linen.

"Our work is difficult and dangerous," he said, drinking his tea and wincing over the pains in his feet. "To find the root one must wander through forest and over mountains almost on one's knees, as the plant is small and hides in the thickest grass. Finally, when you have found the treasured root, you must carefully dig away each inch of earth. At the same time you must beware of the big she-cat (tiger) which, like the panther, also hunts for ginseng. The root gives strength and long life, and that is why these animals seek it and eat it. And when they see it in the possession of a man or a bear, they begin to fight for it and will never retreat until they get it or are killed. I have already been wandering for six years through the taiga, during which time I have killed nine tigers and two panthers, to say nothing of the bears brought down. I am not afraid of the great she-cat, for when I killed the first one, which attacked me on the Mai Ho in a meadow where the roots grew, I ate its heart and liver. But the most terrible of all is the devil who guards the ginseng. He is small and red with burning eyes. In the daytime he protects the roots by blinding the hunter; at night he sets fire to the grass and attaches himself to the breast of the hunter, sucking his blood."

"Have you seen him?" I asked.

"No, but old Fu-chiang saw him twice and his whole breast is scratched by the devil's nails," answered the giant. "It also happens that the devil takes the form of the ginseng root, which appears before the hunter; and when he approaches it, the root retreats farther and farther until the man loses his way and perishes in the forest. A similar experience happened to me last year. I was in ravine looking for the indented leaves of the miraculous plant when suddenly I noticed a big leaf and small red flowers like flamelets. The root was sure to be very old. I came nearer but could not reach it, as the distance to it remained always the same. I followed it into the woods until finally the leaf and flowers disappeared. I looked about everywhere but could discover nothing. As it was almost evening, I wanted to return to the *fansa* but could not make out the way. After wandering till midnight, I sat down, tired and sore, under a tree and was about to fall asleep when I heard some one tramping loudly through the forest. At the time I had no rifle, only an ax, but with this I made ready. Suddenly I saw a bear sniffing about. He raised his head and looked at me, advanced quite near to me, looked in my eyes, and turned and went away. I understood that he called me, and so I followed him and he led me to our stream from which I easily found my way back to

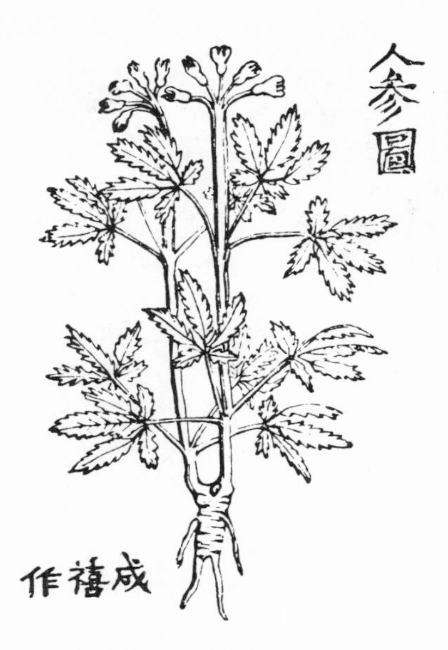

Ginseng: Nineteenth-century Chinese engraving, from E.-R. Huc, *Travels in Tartary, Thibet, and China,* London, 1852.

our *fansa.* Yes, *ta-jen* (sir), in the taiga one can see many strange things."

He rose up with a groan, stretched his huge limbs till the joints cracked, put his rifle on his shoulder, tied his knife and shovel to his belt where already an ax was lodged, and went out. I remarked that as food for the whole day he took only two little *man-t'ou,* small Chinese steamed bread in the form of dumplings.

IMPERIAL LAWS CONCERNING GINSENG *

When the Manchu emperors brought the collection of ginseng under imperial control in the late seventeenth century,

* Jan Jakob Maria de Groot, *The Religious System of China,* vol. 3, book 1, Leiden, 1897, pp. 911–913, 1333.

it was necessary to restrict the number of people who would be allowed to gather the root. One means for accomplishing control was the building and patrolling of the Willow Palisade, a tall wooden fence, along the entire southern boundary of Manchuria, to keep out the Koreans and Chinese who had been used to traveling long distances "east of the pass"—into Manchuria—to search for the most valued variety of wild ginseng. The most valuable ginseng of all was that which grew in the Imperial Cemetery of the Manchus, and laws were made (and eventually codified in the nineteenth century) to punish severely anyone bold enough to hunt for the imperial ginseng. As the Kirin tales show, the Ch'ang-pai Mountains, the sacred range of the Manchus, was the area where the best root had always grown.

The first Emperor of the Ts'ing (or Ch'ing) Dynasty, the Manchu Shun Chih (d. 1661), who mounted the throne of China after the conquest of Peking by his armies in 1644, and most of his successors down to the last Emperor are, together with their chief consorts and concubines, buried in a valley 240 Chinese miles from Peking. This cemetery is officially and popularly designated by the name Tung ling (Eastern Mausolea). It stands against a broad chain of hills, the Ch'ang-shui shan (Hills of Radiant Felicity), over which the Great Wall runs from east to west, forming the northern boundary of the cemetery. The imperial geomancers commanded its situation and discerned in the surrounding hills a compound of qualities able to ensure the dynasty the everlasting possession of the throne, and everlasting peace and prosperity to the nation.

The area was surrounded by three boundaries, marked by red, white, and blue series of posts, the central area, red-posted, containing the tombs themselves. The central area especially is thickly planted with trees, and these provide the shade for the imperial ginseng grown there. All of the ginseng grown in the country belonged to the Emperor, and it was an imperial prerogative to have the imperial root planted in the imperial burying ground.

EXTRACT FROM THE LAWS OF THE GREAT TS'ING DYNASTY: CHAPTER XXV, CRIMINAL LAWS—REBELLION, ROBBERY, AND THEFT: SIXTH SUPPLEMENTARY ARTICLE, ON THEFT OF GINSENG FROM AN IMPERIAL MAUSOLEUM (ENACTED IN 1830).

If Bannermen, civil subjects, or anyone whosoever dig ginseng with thievish intent within the red posts of a mausoleum, to the weight of fifty *taels* * or more, the chief offenders shall come under the fundamental law which provides against stealing Imperial implements assigned for the Great Imperial Sacrifices to Heaven, and be beheaded accordingly, but the Imperial confirmation of the sentence will first have to be obtained. Their accomplices shall be relegated to Turkestan, and there be given as slaves to the soldiery. The chief culprits shall be condemned to this latter punishment if the unearthed ginseng weighs twenty or more *taels,* and their accomplices in this case shall be castigated with one hundred blows with the long stick and be banished for life to a region three thousand miles distant. Should the weight be ten or more than ten *taels,* the punishment for the chief offenders shall be lifelong banishment in a malarious province, viz., Yunnan, Kweichu, Kwangtung, or Kwangsi, and for the accomplices one hundred blows with transportation to a distance of two thousand miles; and should it be ten *taels* or less, the chief culprits shall be banished for life to a country not far distant, and the accomplices be beaten with one hundred blows and be banished for three years.

If ginseng has been dug up without the red posts but within the white ones, the punishment shall be as follows: for a weight of fifty *taels* or more, strangulation of the chief culprits, with

* *Tael:* a weight of silver based upon the Chinese ounce, varying locally according to the customs of a particular trade and district; generally 580 grains troy.

imprisonment until their sentence has been confirmed by the higher authorities, and lifelong banishment of the accomplices to a province not far distant. For twenty *taels* or more, lifelong banishment of the chief offenders to a malarious region and flagellation of the accomplices with one hundred blows, together with lifelong banishment to a region three thousand miles distant. For ten *taels* or more, the chief culprits shall be deported for life to a province not far off, and for a weight of less than ten *taels,* they shall receive one hundred blows with the long stick and be transported for life to a country three thousand miles off [*sic*]; and for each of these quantities the accomplices shall receive one hundred blows and be banished for three years.

And should the digging have taken place outside the white and inside the blue posts, both the chief culprits and the accomplices shall be differently punished in a way such as the supplementary law which provides for those digging in the soil for ginseng with a thievish intent demands.

If no ginseng has been found by the offenders, the punishments above specified in this article for cases in which it has been obtained shall be inflicted with a mitigation of one degree.

Those who have wittingly sold such ginseng shall be punished one degree less severely than the persons who have secretly dug it up, but they shall not be liable to punishment if they have sold it without being aware of its origin.

If in the above cases ginseng has been appropriated, the chief culprits and the accomplices shall all be branded with the characters, "Theft of ginseng belonging to the Government"; but no branding shall take place if no ginseng has been appropriated, nor shall the persons who have sold it be branded. The ginseng and things (that have served for its unearthing?) shall be confiscated by the Government. If Bannermen have committed the offense, they shall be deprived of their Bannermanship and be sentenced according to the laws in force for civil subjects.

Should petty officials or soldiers (charged with guarding of the mausoleum grounds) have willfully connived at the offense for a bribe, they shall be punished in the same degree as the offenders proper, unless the penalty of death has to be inflicted upon these latter. And if the quantity of ginseng is considerable, the punishment required for theft of things of its value shall be calculated and, if it is heavier than the punishments mentioned in this article, be inflicted upon the culprits. Should the offenders proper incur decapitation, the chief culprits among the bribed officials or soldiers shall be condemned to strangulation, and be executed without confirmation of their sentence by higher authorities; but if the offenders have incurred such strangulation, those officials and soldiers shall be sent to Turkestan, there to be placed in different localities in Government thralldom. Those who have merely been remiss in maintaining the regulations with respect to the guarding of the ground shall, if they are soldiers, receive one hundred blows with the long stick, and if they are officials, they shall be delivered over to the Board to which they belong, to be brought up for trial by it.

Mystery of the Ginseng: European Discoveries

Whatever comes from China has always gained a quick hold on the consciousness of Europe. So when the story of a medicinal plant able to cure all of mankind's ills first came to be known to Europeans, it surely demanded attention and investigation. A few Jesuits in the seventeenth century, who had been to China to canvas the territory for missionary activity, reported to the West the existence of ginseng, and as the century progressed, some roots even found their way back to Europe in the earliest days of the China trade.

But no one knew what the plant looked like, and except for a few reports of medical successes like Dr. Simpson's—which was probably dismissed as quackery—investigators remained skeptical of ginseng's medical worth, because they were ignorant of the proper methods of preparation and administration.* It remained for the Jesuit cartographer Jartoux to discover the plant *in situ* on an expedition to Manchuria, and for his discovery to be repeated by another Jesuit, Lafitau, halfway around the world in the Canadian missions. Finally, the Chinese way with ginseng was observed and carefully reported by DuHalde, a dedicated sinologue, more than a century after Europeans first became aware of it.

* The first European experiments with ginseng were reported by J. P. Breynius and Fredericus Dekkers, *Dissertatio botanico-medica de radice gin-sem,* Lugduni Batavorum, 1700. Their book was rather misnamed, for it was not really possible to determine the botanical properties of a dried root, and the results of their medical experimentation were unimaginatively presented and entirely negative.

As soon as the mystery was solved and the plant catalogued (the generic name chosen was *panax,* from *panacea,* cure-all), the European urge to discover was satisfied, and medical experimentation virtually ceased. Nevertheless ginseng became an immensely profitable element of trade and the various East India companies fell over each other to supply North American roots to the insatiable Chinese market. One might argue that a principal reason for ginseng's failure to gain popularity in Europe was that its discovery in America made it an item of commerce and hence of income to European merchants, who would be unlikely to bring ginseng out of China, when they were exerting themselves so to take it in. Ginseng became one of the developing commercial links between China and the West, the economic corollary of tea. Of course it was not destructive to China like smoking opium was—another successful Western introduction—though one could fairly say that Europeans understood it and its effects no better.

SOME

OBSERVATIONS

Made upon the ROOT called

Nean, or Ninſing,

IMPORTED

From the *EAST-INDIES.*

SHEWING

Its wonderful Virtue, in curing *Conſumptions*, *Ptiſſicks*, *Shortneſs of Breath*, *Diſtillation of Rhume*, and reſtoring Nature after it hath been Impaired by Languiſhing Diſtempers, and long Fits of Sickneſs.

Publiſht by a Doctor of Phyſick in *York-ſhire*, in a Letter to Mr. *Colwell*, a Member of the *Royal Society*, 1680.

LONDON,

Printed for the Author.

The author of this early medical opinion on the merits of ginseng is supposed to be William Simpson, a Yorkshire physician and naturopath, author of *Hydrologia Chimica, Hydrological Essays* and *A Treatise upon the Medical Virtues of Scarborough Spaw.*

SOME

OBSERVATIONS

Made upon

The ROOT called *NEAN*, or *NINSING*, &c.

SIR,

I Have read that ſome famous Divines have not ſpared to report in Print, that they believed *Cardan* Phyſician to King *Edward* the Sixth, was now in Hell, becauſe he refuſed to tell the World a Secret with which he wrought great Cures. And therefore for my part, I am reſolved to prevent the Occaſion of any ſuch Cenſure, and freely Communicate this Noble and Excellent Medicine, that hath done ſuch great Cures in *China*, *Japan*, and many other parts of the World, when abundance of compounded Elaborate Remedies have proved ineffectual.

When I lived at *Hull* in *Yorkſhire*, a parcel of it was given me for a Preſent, which I uſed with wonderfull ſucceſs: And particularly, to a Relation of Mr. *Andrew Marvel's*, who was much emaciated, and reduced unto a perfect Skeleton, a meer Bag of Bones, by a long Hectick Feaver, joyned with an Ulcer of the Lungs; being despaired of by all Friends, I was resolved to try what the Tincture of this Root would doe, which I gave every Morning in Red Cows Milk, warm from her Duggs, (which my worthy Friend and intimate Acquaintance, Dr. *Primrose*, preferrs before Asses Milk, as you may see in his Book called *Popular Errors*): And I found his Flesh to come again like that of a Child, and his lost Appetite restored, and his natural Ruddy Complexion revived in his Cheeks, to the Amazement of his desponding Relations, that he was called *Lazarus the Second*.

I solemnly profess, that I hate all Pretences to Secrets, and I look upon the Printed Bills of Quacks, who pretend to *Nostrums*, and private Medicines, to be meer Cheats, and Tricks to amuse the common People, and to pick their Pockets: But if any Man can communicate a good Medicine, he shews himself a Lover of his Countrey more than of himself, and deserves Thanks of Mankind.

And for my part, I verily believe, that next unto the Virtue of *Scarborongh Spaw*, (which I suppose I have sufficiently recommended) I think this is one of the best Medicines in the World, and in many cases better against Consumptions and Distempers of the Lungs than that.

Ogleby in his Natural History of *China*, tells the World, that a Pound of this Root is sold in the Countrey

Countrey wherein it growes, for three times its weight in Silver, it is looked upon as ſo great a Cordial.

And *Piſo* that Learned Phyſician eſteems it a mighty Reſtorer of Nature, and as far as may be a Renewer of Youth.

Publick Fame ſaith, that the Popes of *Rome*, who are choſen to that Office when they are very Old, doe make great uſe of this Root, to preſerve their Radical Moyſture and natural Heat, that ſo they may the longer enjoy their Comfortable Preferments.

I once recommended this Root to my good Friend Mr. *Steel* the Miniſter, with ſingular advantage to his Health, as he told me; but finding him under the Care of an Excellent Phyſician, I adviſed him to lay aſide all Medecins but what he preſcribed.

When I read the Bills of Mortality, and find three or four Thouſand dye in a Year of Conſumptions, notwithſtanding all the rational Methods of Phyſicians, and the boaſting Pretences of Quacks and Mountebanks, I could no longer conceal this Excellent Specifick..

A very conſiderable Perſon at *Hull*, who was very much pined away, had a Cough and Shortneſs of Breath, a Quick Pulſe, and an intenſe Heat, at ſome certain times, with wandering Pains in ſeveral parts of his Body, and reſtleſs Nights, and no Appetite to Food; my Advice being deſired, I wiſht

 him

him to take the Extract made with this Root every Night in Almond-Milk, and in a Months time he grew fat and plump, and all his ill ſymptoms left him, and he is yet alive, to the Glory of God, and the Comfort of his Relations.

One thing is very remarkable, that let the Cauſe of the Conſumption be what it will, *viz.* an Ulcer of the Lungs, or a Scorbutick ſharp Humour in the Blood, or a Hectick Feaver, or the Infection of the Spermatick Veſſels, which in time and in various Diſguiſes ſpoyls the whole Habit of the Body, and by diſabling the parts to digeſt their Nouriſhment, bring Leanneſs and Conſumption; I ſay let any of theſe, or all of them, be Cauſes, yet this Root proves advantageous, as Experience teſtifies.

The Caſe of the Gentlewoman at *Leeds* in *Yorkſhire* is very remarkable, who catching cold in her Lying in, fell under great Weakneſs, a dry Cough, Stitches in her Breſt and Sides, Heat in her Palms and Feet, pining away inſenſibly; many Phyſicians were conſulted, but all in vain; at laſt I adviſed her to take the Spirit made of this Root, about ten Drops at a time, in a Glaſs of old *Mallago* after Dinner. In a ſhort time after ſhe gathered her Fleſh, and had Five Children.

At *Rippon* there was a Good Friend of mine, of a conſiderable Eſtate, whoſe only Child falling into a deep Conſumption upon his Breeding of Teeth, the Parents being almoſt diſtracted for want of an Heir, nothing elſe being expected but Death, and the Child being tyred out with other Medicines, I re-

recommended the Tincture, Spirit and Extract made of this Root; and in six Weeks time the Child mended and grew strong and lusty, and is like to be a Man.

These and many such Examples might be given, which are great Encouragement to make use of such a known, safe, and experienced Remedy, and so very pleasant as this is, being taken only in Drops, whereby it becomes extreamly agreeable unto Children, who pine away upon breeding their Teeth, as daily Experience shews, to the great Grief of many tender Mothers.

A Friend of mine at *York* who buried Six Children, preserved the seventh (under God) with this Root; for it hath no manner of Heat, but is exceeding temperate, and may be given in all their Victuals and Spoon-meat.

Mr. *Boyle* once told me, he thought it was a Medicine sent from Heaven, to save the Lives of Thousands of Men, Women and Children.

FINIS.

*A EUROPEAN DISCOVERS ORIENTAL GINSENG**

Father Jartoux was one of many Jesuits sent to the China missions in the long reign of Emperor K'ang hsi (1661–1722), whose notable interest in science and art and notable lack of xenophobia was the occasion of the opening of his Empire to Western influences. Jartoux was trained as a cartographer and drew for Imperial use the first accurate map of Manchuria. His careful description and drawing of ginseng was the first known to Europe and received wide translation and reproduction. His guess that "if [ginseng] *is to be found in any other country of the world, it may be particularly in Canada" proved, amazingly enough, to be correct: the American species was discovered a few years later near Montreal.*

Peking, April 12, 1711

Reverend Father,

The map of Tartary, which we made by order of the Emperor of China, gave us an opportunity to see the famous plant ginseng, so much esteemed in China and so little known in Europe. Towards the end of July 1709 we arrived at a village not above four small leagues distant from the Kingdom of Korea, which is inhabited by those Tartars called Calca tatze. One of these Tartars went and found upon the neighboring mountains four plants of the ginseng, which he brought us entire in a basket: I took one of them and designed it, in its exact dimensions as well as I could possibly do it; the figure

* [Paul-Emile?] Jartoux, SJ, "The Description of a Tartarian Plant, called Gin-seng; with an Account of its Virtues. In a Letter from Father Jartoux to the Procurator General of the Missions of India and China. Taken from the Tenth Volume of the Letters of the Missionary Jesuits, Printed at Paris in Octavo, 1713," *Philosophical Transactions* [of the Royal Society], *Giving some Account of the Present Undertakings, Studies, and Labours of the Ingenious, in Many Considerable Parts of the World,* vol. XXVIII (1713), London, 1714, pp. 237–247.

of which I here send you, and shall give you the explanation of it at the end of this letter.

The most eminent physicians in China have writ whole volumes upon the virtues and qualities of this plant and make it an ingredient in almost all remedies which they give to their chief nobility, for it is of too high a price for the common people. They affirm, that it is a sovereign remedy for all weaknesses occasioned by excessive fatigues either of body or mind, that it dissolves pituitous humors, that it cures weakness of the lungs and the pleurisy, that it stops vomitings, that it strengthens the stomach and helps the appetite, that it disperses fumes or vapors, that it fortifies the breast, and is a remedy for short or weak breathing, that it strengthens the vital spirits and increases lymph in the blood, in short, that it is good against dizziness of the head and dimness of sight, and that it prolongs life in old age.

Nobody can imagine that the Chinese and Tartars would set so high a value upon this root if it did not constantly produce a good effect. Those that are in health often make use of it to render themselves more vigorous and strong, and I am persuaded that it would prove an excellent medicine in the hands of any European who understands pharmacy, if he had but a sufficient quantity of it to make such trials as are necessary, to examine the nature of it chemically, and to apply it in a proper quantity according to the nature of the disease for which it may be beneficial.

It is certain that it subtilizes, increases the motion of, and warms the blood, that it helps digestion and invigorates in a very sensible manner. After I had designed the root, which I shall hereafter describe, I observed the state of my pulse, and then took half of the root, raw as it was and unprepared: in an hour after I found my pulse much fuller and quicker, I had an appetite, and found myself much more vigorous, and could bear labor much better and more easily than before.

But I did not rely on this trial alone, imagining that this alteration might proceed from the rest that we had that day: but four days after, finding myself so fatigued and weary that

I scarce could sit on horseback, a mandarin who was in company with us perceiving it, gave me one of these roots: I took half of it immediately, and an hour after I was not the least sensible of any weariness. I have often made use of it since, and always with the same success. I have observed also that the green leaves, and especially the fibrous part of them chewed, would produce nearly the same effect.

The Tartars often bring us the leaves of ginseng instead of tea, and I always find myself so well afterwards that I should readily prefer them before the best tea. Their decoction is of a grateful color, and when one has taken it twice or thrice its taste and smell become very pleasant.

As for the root of this plant, it is necessary to boil it a little more than tea, to allow time for extracting its virtue, as is practiced by the Chinese when they give it to sick persons, on which occasion they seldom use more than the fifth part of an ounce of the dried root. But as for those that are in health, and take it only for prevention or some slight indisposition, I would advise them not to make less than ten doses of an ounce, and not to take of it every day. It is prepared in this manner: the root is to be cut into thin slices, and put into an earthen pot well glazed, and filled with about a quarter of a pint of water Paris measure. The pot must be well covered and set to boil over a gentle fire, and when the water is consumed to the quantity of a cupful, a little sugar is to be mixed with it, and it is to be drunk immediately. After this, as much more water is to be put into the pot upon the remainder, and to be boiled as before, to extract all the juice and what remains of the spirituous part of the root. These two doses are to be taken, one in the morning and the other at night.

As to the places where this root grows, because you will see them marked in the new map of Tartary, a copy of which we shall send into France, I shall only observe here in general that it is between the thirty-ninth and forty-seventh degree of northern latitude, and between the tenth and twentieth degree of eastern longitude, reckoning from the meridian of Peking.

There is there a long tract of mountains, which the thick forests that cover and encompass them render almost unpassable. It is upon the declivities of these mountains and in these thick forests, upon the banks of torrents or about the roots of trees, and amidst a thousand other different sorts of plants, that the ginseng is to be found. It is not to be met with in plains, valleys, marshes, the bottoms of rivulets, or in places too much exposed and open. If the forest take fire and be consumed, this plant does not appear till two or three years after. It also lies hid from the sun as much as possible, which shows that heat is an enemy to it. All of which makes me believe that if it is to be found in any other country in the world, it may be particularly in Canada, where the forests and mountains, according to the relation of those that have lived there, very much resemble these here.

The places where the ginseng grows are on every side separated from the province of Kwantung (which in our old maps is called Leaotung) by a barrier of wooden stakes which encompasses this whole province, and about which guards continually patrol to hinder the Chinese from going out and looking after this root. Yet how vigilant soever they are, their greediness after gain incites the Chinese to lurk about privately in these deserts, sometimes to the number of two or three thousand, at the hazard of losing their liberty and all the fruit of their labor, if they are taken either as they go out of or come into the province.

The Emperor, having in mind that the Tartars should have the advantage that is to be made of this plant rather than the Chinese, gave orders this present year 1709 to ten thousand Tartars to go and gather all that they could of the ginseng, upon condition that each person should give His Majesty two ounces of the best, and that the rest should be paid for according to its weight in fine silver. It was computed that by this means the Emperor would get this year about twenty thousand Chinese pounds of it, which would not cost him above one-fourth part of its value. We met by chance with some of these

Tartars in the midst of those frightful deserts, and their mandarins, who were not far distant out of our way, came one after another and offered us oxen for our subsistance, according to the commands they had received from the Emperor.

This army of herbarists observed the following order. After they had divided a certain tract of land among their several companies, each company, to the number of a hundred, spreads itself out in a straight line to a certain fixed place, every ten of them keeping at a distance from the rest. Then they searched carefully for the plant, going on leisurely in the same order, and in this manner in a certain number of days they run over the whole space of ground appointed them. When the time is expired the mandarins, who are encamped with their tents in such places as are proper for the subsistence of their horses, send to view each troop, to give them fresh orders, and to inform themselves if their number is complete. If any one of them is wanting, as it often happens, either by wandering out of the way, or being devoured by wild beasts, they look for him a day or two, and then return again to their labor as before.

These poor people suffer a great deal in this expedition. They carry with them neither tents nor beds, everyone being sufficiently loaded with his provision, which is only millet parched in an oven, upon which he must subsist all the time of his journey. So that they are constrained to sleep under trees, having only their branches and barks, if they can find them, for their covering. Their mandarins send them from time to time some pieces of beef, or such game as they happen to take, which they eat very greedily and almost raw. In this manner these ten thousand men pass six months of the year, yet notwithstanding their fatigues continued lusty and seemed to be good soldiers. The Tartars which were our guard did not fare better, having only what remained of an ox that was killed every day, and had first served fifty persons, for their subsistence.

To give you next an idea of this plant, which the Tartars and Chinese put so great a value upon, I shall explain the

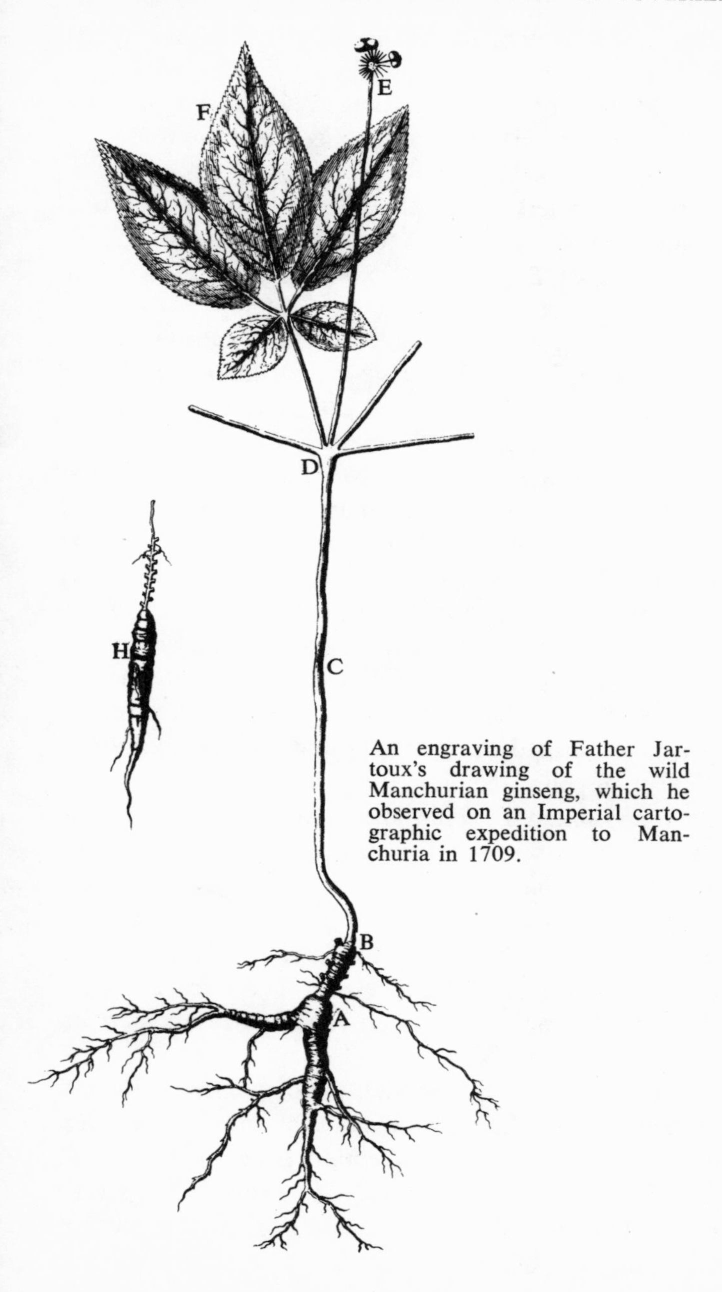

An engraving of Father Jartoux's drawing of the wild Manchurian ginseng, which he observed on an Imperial cartographic expedition to Manchuria in 1709.

figure here sent you, which was drawn with the greatest exactness that was possible.

A shows the root of the plant, which when washed was white and a little rugged and uneven, as the roots of other plants generally are.

BCD represent the length and thickness of the stalk, which is smooth and pretty round, of a deepish red color, except near the beginning at *B,* where it is whiter by reason of its nearness to the ground.

D is a sort of knot or joint made by the shooting out of four branches, which all rise from the same center and divide from one another at equal distances and at the same height from the ground. The underside of the branch is green mixed with white; the upper part is much like the stalk, of a deep red, inclining to the color of a mulberry. These two colors gradually decrease and unite on the sides in a natural mixture. Each branch has five leaves, as represented in the figure. It is remarkable that these branches separate from each other at equal distances, as well in respect of themselves as of the horizon, and make with their leaves a circular figure nearly parallel to the surface of the ground.

Though I have finished the design of but half of one of the leaves at *F,* yet anyone may easily conceive and perfect the rest in the same manner. I do not know that I ever saw leaves so large as these that were so thin and fine: their fibers are very distinguishable, and on the upper side they have some small whitish hairs. The skin between the fibers rises a little in the middle above the level of the fibers. The color of the leaf is a dark green above and a shining whitish green underneath. All the leaves are serrated or very finely indented on the edges.

From *D,* the center of the branches, there rises a second stalk *DE,* which is very straight and smooth, and whitish from bottom to top, bearing a bunch of round fruit of a beautiful red color. This bunch was composed of twenty-four berries, two of which I have here drawn, marked *gg.* The red skin that colors the berry is very thin and smooth; it contains within it a white softish pulp. As these berries were double (for they are sometimes found single) each of them had two rough stones, separated from one another, of the size and figure of our common lentils, excepting that the stones have not a thin edge like lentils, but are almost everywhere of an equal thickness. Each berry was supported by a smooth, even, and very fine sprig, of the color of those of our small red cherries. All these sprigs rose from the same center, and spreading exactly like the rays of a sphere, they make the bunch of berries that they bear of a circular form. This fruit is not good to eat. The stone is like the stones of other common fruit: it is hard, and encloses a kernel. It is always placed upon the same plan or level with the sprig that bears the berry. From whence it is, that the berry is not round, but a little flat on each side. If it be double, there is a kind of depression or hollow place in the middle where the two parts unite. It has also a small beard at top, diametrically opposite to the sprig on which it hangs. When the berry is dry, there remains only a shriveled skin that sticks close to the stones, and is then of a dark red or almost black color.

This plant dies away and springs again every year. The number of its years may be known by the number of stalks it has shot forth, of which there always remains some mark, as may be seen in the figure by the letters *bbb,* &c. From whence it appears that the root *A* was seven years old, and that the root *H* was fifteen.

As to the flower, not having seen it, I can give no description of it. Some say it is white and very small; others have assured me that the plant has none and that no one ever saw it. I rather believe that it is so small and so little remarkable that they never took notice of it, and what confirms me in this opinion is that those that look for the ginseng, having regard to and minding only the root, commonly neglect and throw away the rest of the plant as of no use.

There are some plants which, beside the bunch of berries

I have described, have also one or two berries like the former, placed an inch or an inch and a half below the bunch. And when this happens, they say if anyone takes notice of the point of the compass that these berries direct to, he can't fail of finding the plant at some paces distant that way, or thereabouts. The color of the berries, when the plant has any, distinguishes it from all others and makes it remarkable at first sight; but it sometimes happens that it bears none, though the root be very old, as that marked by the letter *H* had no fruit, though it was in its fifteenth year.

They having sowed the seed in vain, without its producing any plant, might probably give occasion to this story which is current among the Tartars. They say that a bird eats it as soon as it is in the earth, and not being able to digest it, it is purified in its stomach, and afterwards springs up in the place where it is left by the bird with its dung. I rather believe that the stone remains a long time in the ground before it shoots out any root. And this opinion of mine seems the more probable because there are found some roots which are not longer and not so big as one's little finger, though they have shot forth successively at least ten stalks in as many different years.

Though the plant I have here described had four branches, yet there are some that have but two, others but three, and some that have five or seven, which last are the most beautiful. Yet every branch has always five leaves, as well as this here figured, unless the number has been diminished by any accident. The height of the plant is proportionable to their bigness and the number of their branches. Those that bear no fruit are commonly small and very low.

The root, the larger and more uniform it is, and the fewer small strings or fibers it has, is always the better, on which account that marked with the letter *H* is preferable to the other. I know not for what reason the Chinese call it ginseng, which signifies "the representation or form of man." Neither I myself, nor others who have searched and inquired into it on purpose could ever find it had any resemblance to the signification of its name, though among other roots there may now and then be found some which by accident have very odd figures. The Tartars with more reason call it *orhota,* which signifies "the chief of plants."

It is not true that this plant grows in China, as Father Martini affirms from the authority of some Chinese books, which make it to grow on the mountains of Yong-pinsu in the province of Peking. They might easily be led into this mistake because that is the place where it first arrives when it is brought from Tartary into China.

Those that gather this plant preserve only the root, and bury together in some certain place in the earth all that they can get of it in ten or fifteen days' time. They take care to wash it well and cleanse it with a brush from all extraneous matter. Then they dip it into scalding water and prepare it in the fume of a sort of yellow millet, which communicates to it part of its color. The millet is put into a vessel with a little water and boils over a gentle fire; the roots are laid upon small transverse pieces of wood over the vessel and are thus prepared, being covered with a linen cloth or some other vessel placed over them. They may also be dried in the sun or by the fire, but then, though they retain their virtue well enough, yet they have not that color which the Chinese so much admire. When the roots are dried they must be kept close in some very dry place; otherwise they are in danger of corrupting or being eaten by worms.

I wish the description I have here given of the ginseng, so highly esteemed in this Empire, may please you and those to whom you shall impart it. We are now going into Tartary to finish the map of that country, having still the west and northwest part of it to do. I will send you as soon as possible the map of the province of Peking, by Father Martini, called Pekeli, and by the Chinese Tcheli or Lipasu. I am, &c.

JARTOUX

A EUROPEAN DISCOVERS AMERICAN GINSENG *

I never heard ginseng spoken of when I was in France. Yet this famous root has been known in Europe for several years by the reports of some fathers of our Company who were the first to speak of it. These may be seen in the *Chinese Atlas* of Father Martini, in the *Natural History* of Father Eusèbe de Nieremberg, and in the *China Illustrated* of the famous Father Kircher. The French and Dutch ships which have imported it since have made its knowledge more certain.

Thus it was by pure chance that I began to know of ginseng for the first time. I had arrived at Quebec on the business of our mission in October 1715.

The custom is every year to send us a collection of instructive letters from the missionaries of our Company who work in various parts of the world for the salvation of our fellow-beings. . . . Among these letters there are some interesting ones concerning diverse matters bearing on science and the arts, and which often produce useful discoveries for the good of the state and colonies. So in Quebec I received the tenth collection of these letters, and I read with pleasure the one from Father Jartoux. I found in it an exact description of the ginseng plant, which he had occasion to examine during a voyage he had made to Tartary in 1709 . . .

In order to announce the truths of our religion to uncivilized nations, and make them taste of a morality very opposed to the corruption of their hearts, we first have to win them over, and to insinuate ourselves into their spirits by becoming neces-

* Joseph-François Lafitau, SJ, *Mémoire Présenté à Son Altesse Royale Monseigneur le Duc d'Orléans, Régent du Royaume de France, Concernant la Précieuse Plante du Gin-seng de Tartarie, découverte en Canada par le P. Joseph-François Lafitau, de la Compagnie de Jésus, Missionnaire des Iroquois du Sault Saint Louis,* Paris, 1718, pp. 5–18 *passim.*

sary to them. Several of our missionaries have succeeded in different places because they have a certain talent for medicine. I know that while working to cure the ills of the body they have been lucky enough in some cases to open the eyes of the soul. They have often used this means to baptize many dying children, under the pretext of giving them some medication. Thus I applied myself very seriously to medicine, which the savages * are very curious about, for although they have some very good remedies of their own they would rather use ours. I felt very attracted to plant lore, which made me read Father Jartoux's letter in preference to other letters in the same collection. Going through this letter, I came upon the place where the Father says, speaking of the nature of the soil where ginseng grows, that if some were to be found in some other part of the world, it would be mainly in Canada, where the forests and mountains, from the reports of people who have been there, are rather similar to those of Tartary. I felt my curiosity aroused by the hope of discovering it in New France.

Yet this hope was rather weak and made little impression on me. I got from the letter only a very confused and imperfect idea of the plant. The work I had during the winter, which is very long and harsh in Canada, almost succeeded in erasing it from my mind. It was only in the spring that, being often obliged to pass through the woods, I felt anew the desire to make this discovery, at the sight of the great multitude of plants which fill these forests and which attracted a good deal of my attention. I tried to recall the ideas I had formed of it. I spoke to several savages. I described the plant to them as best I could remember it. They gave me reason to hope that I could actually discover it.

Necessity has made the savages doctors and herbalists: they

* Lafitau's word is of course *sauvage,* which had no bestial connotation at the time he was writing. The word came from Late Latin *salvaticus,* "forest *dweller*" < L *silva,* "forest," and meant generally "one who is in a state of nature." Lafitau would not have used *indien,* which until the end of the eighteenth century meant "a person born in, or an inhabitant of, the Indies."

seek out plants with curiosity and try them all, so that without the help of a reasoned natural philosophy they have found through long use, which takes the place of science with them, many of the remedies necessary to their ills. Besides the general remedies everyone has his own particular ones which he guards jealously. Truly, nothing is more able to win credit among them than the quality of a good doctor. One must admit that they have some admirable secrets for illnesses which our medicine cannot even touch. Of course they treat themselves in rather a rude fashion, administering their purgatives and emetics to each other as if they were horses, but they excel in treating all kinds of wounds and fractures, which they do with an extreme patience and a delicacy all the more marvellous in that they never use the knife. They cure their sick in a short time by the cleanliness which they maintain in a wound: it always appears to be clean, and the remedies they apply to it are simple, natural and easy to learn. . . .

My questioning of the savages about ginseng did not advance me much. It did not profit me much, but did allow me to make other discoveries which I hope to put into practice when I return to my mission. I flatter myself that I may soon be able to give some knowledge to the public which will please lovers of botany, and from which our medicine might draw some information.

Having spent three months looking for ginseng to no avail, chance showed it to me when I thought of it least, and rather close to a house that I was building. It was then in its maturity; the vermilion of the fruit caught my eye. I looked at it for a short time and immediately thought that this might be the plant I was looking for. I eagerly dug it up, and joyfully carried it to a woman I had employed to look for it. She recognized it right away as one of their ordinary remedies, and described its use among the savages. After my report on the esteem in which it was held in China, she cured herself the following day of an intermittent fever which had tormented her for several months. She did nothing else than to drink cold water in which had been soaked several of these roots, which she had crushed with stones. She has twice since done the same thing, and each time accomplished the cure the same day.

Whatever idea I had that the plant was ginseng, I still could not assure myself of it, having only confused ideas about Father Jartoux's letter, which was not with me but in Quebec. So I wrote down an exact description of the plant I had found, and sent it to an intelligent man in Quebec, for him to compare with the letter and with the engraved plate representing the Chinese ginseng.

No sooner had he received my letter than he left for Montreal, and appeared at our mission, which is three leagues away. The clever man and I wandered through the woods, where I left him the pleasure of discovering the plant himself. Our search was not long. When we had gathered several roots we went and compared them with the book in a cabin.

At the sight of the plate the savages recognized their Canadian plant. And as we had before us the different species, we had the pleasure of seeing such an exact depiction and such a just proportion with our plant, that there was no doubt we had the proof before our eyes.

I was greatly surprised, at the end of Father Jartoux's letter, to learn the explanation of the Chinese word which means "man's image," or as Father Kircher's translator explains, "man's thighs," for I realized that the Iroquois word *garentoguen* has the same meaning. This is a word compounded of *orenta,* which means thighs and legs, and *oguen,* which means two separated things. I had the same reflection as Father Jartoux as to the strangeness of this name, which relates only to a very imperfect resemblance not found at all in many plants of the species, and is a resemblance found in many plants of other species, so I could only conclude that the same meaning could not have been applied in the Chinese and Iroquois words without a communication of ideas, and by consequence of persons. By this I was confirmed in an opinion which I already had, which is based on other judgments, that America made one continent with Asia, united at Tartary to the north of China . . .

GINSENG IN MANCHU CHINA *

Jean-Baptiste DuHalde, SJ, was an encyclopedist, whose four-volume collection of information and lore about China was widely translated and respected in the eighteenth century. "A Geographical, Historical, Chronological, Political and Physical Description of the Chinese Empire and of Chinese Tartary" (Paris, 1735) presented to the West, by then insatiably curious about China and everything Chinese, the greatest amount of information amassed until that time, much of it from Chinese printed sources. The lengthy section on ginseng is in DuHalde's typically conclusive and authoritative style, laden with references to Chinese authorities, medical texts, place names and herbs, all totally obscure to his readers. The chapters reproduced here are followed by a recipe collection, "nine ancient recipes and sixty-eight modern ones," each of which employs ginseng, to cure everything from hemorrhages to consumption, from bleeding gums to dog bites. But the ingredients were unobtainable in the West.

DuHalde hardly mentions the ginseng from southern Manchuria, now and for two hundred years the most valued variety: in his time the forests of Shantung and Leaotung were in large part still standing, and much ginseng grew beneath. The progressive deforestation of northeast China during the reigns of the Manchu emperors meant that the search for ginseng had to be extended northward, into the trackless vastness of the Manchurian wilderness.

The book called *Pi lo* says: ginseng grows in the mountains

* J.-B. DuHalde, "Du Gin Seng, Plante du Premier Ordre dans la Médicine Chinoise; de sa nature, de ses qualitez, & des différentes Recettes qui apprennent l'usage qu'on en fait," *Description géographique, historique, chronologique, politique, et physique de l'Empire de la Chine et de la Tartarie Chinoise,* Paris, 1735, vol. III, pp. 460 ff.

of Shantung and in Leaotung; they gather the root during the first ten days of the second, fourth, and eighth months. They put it out to dry in the sun, without exposing it to the wind. The root has the figure of a man, and is of a spirituous nature.

Pu says: it grows also at Han chan. In the third month it puts out leaves, which are small and pointed. Its branches are black, and the stem is covered with a nap. They gather the root in the third and ninth months. This root has the hands, feet, face, and eyes of a man; it abounds in spirits.

Hong king says: Shantung is to the southeast of I chu. The root which comes from there today is long and yellow. It resembles the remedy called *fang fong*. It is full of a thick, sweet juice. That which is most esteemed now is from Pe tsi. It is small, firm, and white; it does not have a taste as strong as that from Shantung.

They give the second place in use to that from Korea and from Leaotung. From there the root is large, but empty of juice and soft: it is not comparable to that from Pe tsi and Shantung. This plant puts out only one stem, which grows straight up. The leaves are either four by four or five by five. The flower is violet in color.

The inhabitants of Korea, in their praise of ginseng, say: the branches which are born of my stem are three in number and my leaves are five by five. I turn my back to the south and I look toward the north. Whoever would find me must look for the *kia chu; kia chu* and ginseng seek each other out. This *kia* resembles the *lu tong*.* It grows very high and throws a great shade. In these kinds of places ginseng grows in abundance. There is much art in gathering ginseng and in preparing it. Some of it is found at present in the mountains bordering the province of Kiangnan, but it is not much used. . . .

Sun says: the ginseng that the Kingdom of Sinlo pays as tribute has feet and hands, and resembles a man. It is more than a foot long: they keep it pressed between wooden planks

* *Lu tong* is a species of sycamore.

of the tree called *cha mu,* which is a kind of pine, bound and wrapped in red silk. The ginseng of Cha chu has a small short root; it is worthless to use.

Sung says: all the territory of Shansi which is to the east of the Yellow River and Mount Tai chan produces ginseng. That which they bring in under the name of ginseng of Sinlo from parts of Shansi and Honan north of the Yellow River, as well as that from Fukien, are not worth that from Shantung. It begins to grow in the spring. It is found much in the northern parts of great mountain chains. It is born in marshy places.

When it begins to grow, and is only three or four inches high, it sends forth a branch with five leaves; at the end of four or five years it sends forth a second with an equal number of leaves; however it still has neither stem nor flowers. After ten years are accomplished it puts forth a third branch, and after a long period of years a fourth; each has its five leaves. Then it begins to produce a stem from the middle, which they commonly call *pe che chu,* that is to say the pestle with a hundred feet.

During the third and fourth months it bears small flowers the size of a grain of millet, whose filaments resemble silk: they are a violet color, tending toward white. They bear seed after the autumn to the number of six or seven grains, of the size of the *ta teu,* a kind of pea or bean. These seeds are at first green but become red as they ripen; when they are completely ripe they come loose and fall by themselves, and the plant reproduces itself.

The root has the figure of a man, and is very spirituous. The stem and leaves of the ginseng which grows on Mount Tai chan are a violet color; the root is white. Moreover, in the territory which lies between the Hwai and Kiang Rivers, there originates another species of ginseng whose stem, when it shoots forth, is one or two feet high. It bears leaves shaped like little teaspoons, but smaller and resembling those of *ki ken* (plant name). In one place five to seven of these plants may grow at once. The root resembles that of *ki ken* as well, but it is softer and its odor is sweeter and more agreeable. In autumn it bears violet-colored flowers, tending toward green. They dig the root in spring, and in the autumn the country people mix it with other roots and sell it.

In order to recognize the true ginseng of Shantung, they do the following experiment: two persons travel together, one walks with ginseng in his mouth, the other walks with his mouth empty. At the end of half a league he who has the ginseng in his mouth feels no difficulty in breathing, while the other is tired and completely out of breath. This is a certain sign of the goodness of ginseng.

Tsong tchi says: the ginseng of Shantung has a long and thin root: it sometimes reaches more than a foot into the earth, and often splits into ten divisions. It is sold for its weight in silver.* It is a little difficult to find: when the country people have discovered a place where there is some growing, and have gathered a sufficient quantity, they put it between little planks which they wrap in taffeta.

Kia meu says: the ginseng of the Tse tuen Mountains resembles a man. It is violet in color and a little flat. That from Pe tsi is firm, white and perfectly round: they call it *pe tsiao sen,* ram's horn. That from Leaotung is yellow, full of juice, long and thin. It has fibers in the shape of a beard: they commonly call it *hwang seng,* or yellow ginseng: it is better than the others.

The ginseng of Korea tends a little toward violet: it is not firm. That from Sinlo is a tin-colored yellow; it does not have much taste; its figure resembles that of a man, and it is very spirituous. That of the species which is shaped like a chicken's foot has an extraordinary efficacy.

Che chin says: the ancient country of Shantung is that which they call today Lu chu. The people look upon ginseng as the ruin of the country where it grows, because absolutely everything they collect is for the Emperor. That is why they have stopped cultivating it.

That which they use now comes from Leaotung, Korea, Pe

* That was true before, but now it is sold for almost its weight in gold.

tsi and Sinlo, which are dependent on Chao sien or King ki tao [Seoul], capital of Korea. From that which people come into China to sell they can gather the seeds and sow them about the tenth month, using the same methods they customarily employ when they sow pot-herbs.

That which is gathered in autumn and winter is firm and full of juice. On the contrary, that which is gathered in spring and summer is soft and empty of juice. This difference comes not from the good or bad quality of the soil, but from the time in which it is gathered.

The ginseng of Leaotung, when it still has its skin, is a glossy yellow color like *fang fong*. When they remove the skin, it is firm and white like pea-flour. Those who sell it mix it with three kinds of root, *cha seng, tse ni* and *ki keng*. The root *cha seng* is a juiceless substance, has neither spirit nor heart, and an insipid taste. The *tse ni* has neither juice nor heart. The *ki keng* is firm, but its taste is bitter. Ginseng is a juicy substance, hearty; its taste, which is sweet, is joined with a little bitterness, which makes it agreeable to the palate.

That ginseng whose taste is exquisite is commonly called "golden well with low railing of precious stones." That which has the shape of a man is called *hai elb seng* or child's ginseng. This kind is found more often counterfeited than other sorts.

That whose picture is reproduced in the herbal *Sung su sung,* made in the Sung Dynasty by woodcut, engraved with three branches whose leaves are five by five, under the name of ginseng of Lu ngan fu, is the true ginseng . . .

That which is called ginseng from the territory between the Hwai and Kiang Rivers, is likewise *tse ni*. We commonly confuse it with real ginseng because of not examining it closely.

At present ginseng is no longer found at Lu ngan fu, and you should be very careful in taking as true ginseng that which comes from other places. Today there are cheats, who infuse the ginseng in water and draw out all the juice; then they dry the root and sell it. It has no strength, and can be of no use. Therefore you should examine it well for fear of being cheated.

Tche yong, who was formerly an officer in the College of

Court Physicians, left us a treatise on ginseng in two volumes, where he describes in great detail all the characteristics of ginseng, the most remarkable of which you'll find in the following paragraphs.

HOW TO KEEP GINSENG

Song king says: ginseng easily breeds worms. If you want to keep it for a year without its spoiling, you have only to close it up in a new container, and stopper it well.

Ping says: when ginseng is continually exposed to wind and sun, it easily breeds insects; to preserve it you must close it up in an earthen jar which has been used for keeping gingelly [sesame] oil. First wash it and soak it until it is clean. You must then mix with the ginseng some *hwa in* and *si sin* (plant names), and finally seal the container opening. Now you can keep it for a whole year. You can also keep it in ordinary ashes, after having washed it and dried it by the fire, closing up the roots, one with another, in a well-stoppered container.

Li yen says: ginseng grows in such a way that the back of its leaves face the sky: it loves neither sun nor wind. Whenever you take it raw, you put it in your mouth with no other preparation, and chew it.

When you want to prepare it, it must be dried by the fire on a sheet of paper, or put to soak in a kind of wine called *Shun tsyu*. Then crush it, and after warming, use it.

Ginseng should not be kept in iron containers, nor prepared with instruments of the same metal. I have nevertheless fairly often seen it cut without all these precautions, and with a knife.

THE TASTE AND QUALITIES OF THE GINSENG ROOT

The root is sweet, and only a little cooling. It has absolutely no harmful quality.

Pu says: Shin nong ascribes a small degree of coldness to ginseng; Tong kiun and Luei cong attribute bitterness to it. Emperor Hwang ti and Ki pe attribute sweetness to it, and have never noticed any dangerous quality to it (poison).

Yuen su says: its nature is temperate, it has sweetness mixed with a little bitterness, its taste and spirits are light and subtle: they are very volatile. It is the purest spirit of the gross matter (of the imperfect yin). He says elsewhere that it is the least pure spirit of the subtle matter (of the perfect yang).

Chi tsai says: *fu lin* and *ma lin* (plant names) are officers of ginseng. This root has an antipathy to salts and to soils full of vitriol. *Li lu* (plant name) is the opposite.

Ywen su says: ginseng mixed with *shin ma* (seed of a plant), which serves as a vehicle, and taken by mouth, repairs the spirits of the chest, and dissipates unnatural heat in the lungs.

Ginseng taken with *fu lin* repairs the radical moisture of the abdomen, and dissipates heat from the kidneys. It cools the kidneys when taken with scorzonera. It revives the pulse if one mixes it with dry ginger, and strengthens the vital and animal spirits.

Meu says: ginseng taken with *hwang ki* and liquorice is a gentle remedy. Because this mixture is temperate it assuages the heats of fever, causes hot and humid vapors to be exhaled: it restores radical moisture. It is also an excellent remedy for those with boils and external tumors.

Chin ken says: *li lu* has a great opposition to ginseng. By mixing only a tenth of an ounce of the former with an ounce of the latter, you will take away all its virtue.

THE VIRTUES, PROPERTIES, AND EFFECTS OF THE GINSENG ROOT

It strengthens the noble parts; it maintains the body in a healthy state; it fixes the animal spirits; it stops palpitations caused by sudden frights; it drives away malignant vapors; it clears the eyesight; it opens and dilates the heart; it strengthens the judgment. When you take it over a long period of time it makes the body light and fit, and prolongs life. This comes from the great author himself, that is to say from Shi chin.

It warms a cold stomach and intestines; it cures pains and swellings in the belly; it remedies illnesses of the heart, obstructions in the chest, any looseness that occurs, whether from the bowels or by vomiting. It restores the stomach's superior orifice, prevents the dropsy, removes obstructions from the vessels, dissolves calluses which form inside the intestines, penetrates into the blood and veins and quenches thirst. This is drawn from various authors.

It is excellent for curing all kinds of illnesses which weaken and emaciate the body, likewise for enervation caused by excessive physical or mental labor. It stops vomiting, and illnesses of the heart. It strengthens the noble parts, and in general all the vital organs. It dissolves phlegm in the stomach and cures weak lungs. It is good against the malignant fevers of the cold seasons, when they are accompanied by vomiting; against fainting, and interrupted and troubled sleep caused by dreams and phantoms. You must continue to take it for a long time. This is drawn from the author Chin kuen.

It assists digestion, awakens the appetite, regulates the superior opening of the stomach, restores the vital and animal spirits. It is an antidote to poison drawn from stones and metals. This is from Ta ming.

It strengthens weakened lungs, corrects weak and shallow breathing, asthma and shortness of breath. It takes away heat from heart, lungs, liver and stomach. It quenches thirst and produces lymph in the blood. In a word, it is good against all kinds of illnesses of both sexes, proceeding from lack of spirits or weakness. It cures fevers accompanied by sweating. It is good against vertigo, dimness of sight, pains in the head, stomach disorders and vomiting, intermittent fever, diarrhea and tenesmus, against exhaustion and weariness, wind and inflammation of the bowels, spitting and vomiting of blood, and against all kinds of illnesses peculiar to women, both before and after pregnancy.

DuHalde next presents the recipe and directions for ginseng electuary. The quantities of the root used in the two cures described here suggest that such treatment was intended only for the very wealthy. Ginseng was usually generally available from Chinese apothecaries, but its scarcity meant that it was never cheap. The rarest roots cost more than their weight in gold.

GINSENG ELECTUARY

Take ten ounces of ginseng, cut into small slices. Put it to infuse in twenty medium-sized porcelain containers of fountain or river water until it is thoroughly soaked, and pour everything into a silver or stone vessel: boil it over a slow fire made from walnut or mulberry wood until half the water is used up. Then, having drawn off what is left of the juice, pour over the dregs ten medium-sized porcelain containers of water, until they should be reduced to five. Take this juice, and add five containers of water to the ten containers that you have already drawn off. Boil it over a gentle fire until it forms itself into an electuary, which you will then put up in a pot. Use this electuary by stirring the proper dose into the right preparation for the illness in question.

Tan ki says: a man, completely weakened by debauchery, had fallen incurably ill. By means of a bouillon made with green ginger and the skin of a fruit called *cu pi* [orange], into which I stirred some ginseng electuary, I completely cured him.

Ching hiong, being attacked by a kind of tenesmus brought on by excessive debauchery, suddenly fainted and lost his senses. He had extraordinarily stiff hands and dull eyes: an abundant sweat came from his body. The phlegm in his throat made the same noise as a cutting saw. He no longer retained his urine and had a high and completely irregular pulse. All these symptoms evidently indicated an almost complete exhaustion of radical moisture. I promptly had some of this ginseng electuary prepared and applied eighteen cauteries of a kind of wormwood [moxibustion] to the reservoir which is in the abdomen just below the navel, which they call the sea of spirits. Immediately the left hand recovered its movement. After I applied two other cauteries the lips and mouth began to move a little. Immediately I had him take a middling dose of ginseng electuary. Near midnight I had him take three others, after which his eyes began to move. He had not taken three pounds of it when his speech returned. After he had taken five pounds the tenesmus stopped, and after ten pounds he found himself completely cured. If he had been treated like one who had an apoplexy, he would be a dead man.

A person had an abscess in the back; after he had taken the medicine called *neui to she suen* the abscess broke and gave out a quantity of pus, which was followed by much vomiting and fever. The six pulses of his two hands were deep, stiff and strong, all bad symptoms in these cases. I gave him immediately some ginseng electuary diluted with water distilled from fresh-cut bamboo. We used sixteen pounds of ginseng and cut more than a hundred feet of bamboo, after which he found himself well.

Ten days later a violent wind came up and the abscess again formed itself, and filled up with matter. There appeared in the middle a red line, which passed under the shoulder blade and ended at the right ribs. I instantly ordered some ginseng electuary to be made, for him to take with preparations of *dong kwei* and the rind of *cu pi,* adding to it some bamboo water and ginger juice. After he had drunk three pounds of this drug, the abscess opened and the patient was cured.

If after an abscess opens the patient finds his blood and spirits exhausted, if he vomits and can take nothing, or has other unfavorable symptoms, he must take ginseng, *hwang ki, dong kwei* and *pe chu* in equal quantities, which when boiled down to the consistency of an electuary makes an excellent remedy.

"Shangin" in America

Much ginseng was exported from New France in the eighteenth century, but comparatively little came from the British colonies to the south. Independence was no sooner won, however, than the American China trade began in earnest. The first boat to ply the trade, the *Empress of China,* set sail from New York for Canton in 1784 with a cargo made up entirely of wild ginseng, which was exchanged for silk and tea. As the Northwest Territory was explored, ginseng was found in profusion: it was dug up, dried, shipped east, and exported as soon as it was found. No reliable figures exist for the whole of the nineteenth century, but from 1820 to 1903 nearly 17 million pounds of wild American ginseng root were sent out of the country, making many merchants, and a few lucky hunters, very rich indeed.

As with everything else that the white settlers exploited in the new land, the supply of ginseng eventually gave out. When this happened, around the end of the last century, many people began to grow their own from seed. Publications for ginseng growers were quickly started, government and university experimental stations tried to tell people how to establish just the right conditions for the delicate plant to flourish, all to keep the primary element in the China trade from disappearing. It was to no avail. For during the wet summer of 1904 several fungus diseases appeared in the ginseng beds throughout the country. The blights were nearly impossible to eradicate, and in the course of the next few years millions of dollars of investment in American cultivated ginseng were lost: nature's revenge is rarely so swift and sure.

Some clever growers persevered, fought the diseases, and won. Even today a few thousand pounds of American cultivated ginseng are exported each year. But you can walk for many miles in the Appalachian forests, and in those of the Ohio and Mississippi valleys, without finding a trace of the ginseng that once grew there in such profusion.

COLONEL BOONE GETS HIS GINSENG WET

A year or so after he lost the land he had found and settled in Kentucky, because of his failure to lay proper claim to it, Daniel Boone, now residing on the Kanawha River in western Virginia, decided to enter commerce, and make a killing in the ginseng trade. The usually adulatory biographies of Boone seldom mention this adventure, which shows him just as ready to exploit the riches of the new country as the most avid land speculator or New York merchant.

The substance of this story comes from interviews which Lyman C. Draper, an amateur historian and keen admirer of the great frontiersman, had with Col. and Mrs. Nathan Boone, Daniel's son and daughter-in-law, in 1851, about thirty years after Boone's death.

During the fall of 1787 and the winter of 1787–1788—because of the developing China trade, the price of ginseng had been rising steadily for a couple of years in the Philadelphia and New York markets—"Colonel Boone," says Draper, "was busily employed in digging a quantity of *gingsang*—employing several hands, and in buying up what he could. The men employed, Colonel Boone, and his sons who were old enough, camped out among the hills to facilitate the digging." This digging would have taken place in the hills of western Virginia (now West Virginia) and eastern Kentucky. Boone had almost never gotten along very well with his Indian neighbors, having expropriated without any payment much of their best land, so it is doubtful that any of the men employed to dig ginseng were Indians, as had often been the case earlier in the century.

"By the ensuing Spring," Draper continues, "he had some 12 or 15 tons," which, as anyone can tell, is a very large amount of ginseng indeed. He had worked out a way of drying it as well, knowing that the root would quickly spoil undried, and that leaving the drying to the merchants would have cut into his profits considerably. But it is not clear whether the fifteen tons represents dried or fresh weight.

"He loaded a keel boat, and started up the [Ohio] river with his family with him, destined for Philadelphia to market . . . At the head of the large Island just above Gallipolis [Ohio], and the only Island between Gallipolis and Point Pleasant [W.Va.], in attempting to cross the strong current at the head of the island, the boat careened upon the driftwood at the head of the island, and filled with water in shallow water: no lives were lost, but every thing in the boat got wet, and the gingsang much damaged: sending to Point Pleasant, some 3 miles distant, for aid to raise the boat, John Van Bibber and others came to his aid. [He] dried some of the ginsang spread on shore, but all was injured, so he did not get half price; besides, the delay at Point Pleasant caused him to reach Philadelphia immediately after a fall in the price. As it was, Colonel Boone lost by the operation. All had to be washed when dug, strung and dried in the sun."

Boone was not aware of the best way of curing the roots, which did not only include sun drying. Even at a price of ten cents a pound (an average New York price in the late eighteenth century) he would have realized three thousand dollars, an enormous sum of money in the 1780s. At any rate, this setback to his entrepreneurial activities did not daunt him much. The next year found him still digging ginseng, still trying to get a profit from it, still not succeeding at the business. The following is a letter to his friend Col. Thomas Hart, a Maryland merchant or middleman whom Boone had used for other business ventures. Boone's interesting phonetic spelling is retained.

Grate Conhowway [Kanawha]
July the 30h 1789

[to] Col. Hartt & Rochester
Deer Col.

I after My Best Wishes to you & family also Col Rochesters I cannot help Reflecting a Litel on the Downfall of ginsagn wch ware a Litel unfortenit Last fall But I Doubt it will be worse this But the information Come to me in Tolerable good Time altho I had took in a goodel. Sir I wish to have a Later from you in Respect to my Horsis as I am agooddel Concarned a Bout Brothers Debts pray wrigh me and Direct the Later to this place I am Sir with Respect your very Omble Sarvant

Daniel Boone*

THE GINSENG DIGGER †

I was on my way home one August day from Spruce Hut to a farmer's house a couple of miles across the hills to look at a bird dog that I had seen advertised for sale in the village newspaper. While crossing a piece of thick woods about half way to my destination, I found myself looking for ginseng almost unconsciously, for I had seen a ginseng digger selling a sack of roots to a druggist the day before. Most of the small lots of the root reach the market through the hands of the local dealers.

In a particularly shady spot I came upon nearly a dozen stalks of this plant and sat down to dig them up with an interest I had never felt before. Seeing the druggist paying a substantial

* Draper's account of his interview is taken from MS. 6S, pp. 167 f., 330 of the Lyman C. Draper Collection in the State Historical Society of Wisconsin, Madison; Boone's letter is from MS. 14C, p. 92 of the same collection.

† Frank Farrington, "The Ginseng Digger," *The Outing Magazine*, vol. LX (Sept. 1912), pp. 738–742.

Dec. 15, 1916.

GENTLEMEN:

For the benefit and convenience of our Chinese friends and customers, we beg to announce that we have opened up a new store at 37 A Mott Street, in the heart of Chinatown, New York City.

It is our aim to spread satisfaction among our customers who desire to buy from us. We will guarantee our merchandise to be up to the high standard quality of our representation, if not, money will be cheerfully refunded.

Send in your name and address and we will put you on our mailing-list.

Those who have friends in China, or those contemplating going back, remember, Ginseng Root makes a very handsome gift. No orders too large or too small. No extra charge for packing each package separately.

Trusting to be favored with your business and soliciting your correspondence, we beg to remain,

Yours very truly,

THE NEW WORLD GINSENG CO.

Advertisement from *The Chinese Student's Monthly,* an American publication. Of course, ginseng can still be found in Chinese pharmacies in Chinatown, but now it is likely to be Korean or even Manchurian root sold there, rather than American.

sum of money for a simple root that grows wild in the woods around here had impressed my mind with the value of the faculty of observation.

I had always known that ginseng had a spectacular value, but I had never before seen that value cashed in, and it surprised me. Here I found several roots of good size; perhaps they would when dry bring two or three dollars, and I was stumbling upon them right out in the woods. It was just like finding so many silver dollars lying under the leaves with the eagle's tail feathers sticking up in sight.

Whether the Chinese worship the odd-shaped roots of the *Panax quinquefolium* or value it for its medical properties is not important. The main point is that they are willing to pay an exhorbitant price for it and this keeps many a country boy's eyes open during the summer season for the five-leaved stalks and the scarlet berries that grow here and there in the deeper woods.

A fat, tapered little root that is sometimes bisected until it in a way resembles the figure of a man, the ginseng roots when dried will, if clean and white, bring ten dollars a pound.

Many years ago, when all the ginseng that China used was what grew within its own borders, the price was said to be the weight of the roots in gold, and the first cargo taken to Canton from North America produced fabulous profits.

The dried root has so little real medicinal value that it is practically worthless in that respect. It possesses a pleasant, spicy taste, but its money value depends entirely upon sentiment. When the ginseng is at its best there are many men in the Eastern States who for a month or two make a business of digging the roots. They are men of the class who trap for a living in the fall and gain their livelihood from the woods through as much of the year as possible.

I dug away at my find with deep interest and as I dug I paid no heed to anything else, so wrapped up was I in my task of grubbing real money out of the ground. I brushed off the roots and laid them in a row on a stone and when I had finally secured the entire family I gave a sigh of satisfaction and sat up, thinking, "Well, that ought to go quite a way toward paying for that bird dog." As I straightened out my back and looked around I started involuntarily at the sight of the figure of a roughly dressed, unshaven stranger before me, carrying a stout canvas sack over his shoulder and a hickory stick in one hand.

Before I could speak, he said, "You'd better give me them roots. I was just comin' after 'em."

"You came just a little too late," said I.

"Not so you'd notice it," said the stranger. "I ain't been letting that little bunch o' 'shang grow there all summer for you to dig. Hand 'em over!"

Now, I am not of a troublesome disposition. I never raised my hand against any man that I can remember, and I want nothing that is not mine by perfect right.

"Don't be all day about it," the fellow said.

He advanced toward me, dropping his sack behind him and carrying the hickory stick at an angle that might easily have been construed as threatening. I got in front of my own little pile of roots and inquired, with no sign of yielding, "Are these your woods?"

"That's nothing to you. That there 'shang is mine whether these woods are or not, and, what's more, I'm going to have it."

"Well, stranger," said I calmly, "I have not yet disputed any of your statements. This ginseng may be yours some time. It certainly is not yet. Sit down!" and I indicated a rock near by. "I'd like to talk this over with you."

"I ain't here to make any afternoon call. I'm here to get the goods," he replied, with only a very little weakening of his bluff manner.

"Are you a ginseng digger?" I asked him.

"Just now I am and I'm a good one, too. I get what I go after."

"Well, there's no reason why you and I should quarrel," I went on. "Come over here and sit down and fill your pipe and let's talk this over. You look to me like a pretty sensible chap and I know you're good at a bargain, because I saw you selling ginseng to the druggist yesterday afternoon."

As I spoke I filled my pipe and tossed the bag of tobacco

to the man, and at last he came over and seated himself rather gingerly where I had indicated. He clung to his stick, however, and he watched me closely.

"What kind of a game you tryin' to play?" he asked.

"I'm not playing any game. I merely want to arbitrate, that's all."

"Well, you might as well arbitrate that 'shang there into my bag, then, because you needn't think you're going to talk me out of it."

As he said this he handled the hickory stick lovingly.

"Will you let me go my way with my little pocketful of roots," I asked, "if I can get you to offer them to me?"

He was willing to agree to that much, and as he did so he even smiled in a grim kind of way.

This was not the kind of tête-à-tête that one would pick out for a pleasant afternoon in the woods, but, after all, I was interested in this uncouth specimen and I realized that his point of view might be sufficiently different from my own to be of interest.

"How much root do you get in a season?" I inquired.

"Well, sometimes more an' sometimes less. I ain't had no luck this year. I guess there's a blight struck the plants."

"What do they do with these roots?" I asked further.

"Oh, the Chinks worship 'em and when they're shaped like a man they say they'll give 'most any price for 'em. They all bring the same by weight, though. Who are you, anyway? You seem to have a lot o' questions to ask."

"Oh," said I, "I live over here in the woods some of the time. Why don't you come over and see me? You know the little shanty over that ridge by the swamp?"

"Yes, I know. I come by there yesterday and someone was inside building a fire. Must 'a' been you."

"I presume it was. Why didn't you come in?"

"I guess you don't know me, do you?"

I admitted that I did not.

"I'm one o' them Scrammels from over in the Beaverkill country."

I had heard of the Scrammels. "Them Scrammels" they were

generally termed. They were a family of rough mountaineers who had an unusually bad name. Their reputation was of the sort that caused every minor depredation in their locality to be laid to them, and I think they probably were usually guilty.

In every community there are two or three families, or perhaps but one, that must bear the blame for all kinds of deviltry, from robbing a henroost or a clothesline to breaking into the bank.

"Come on home with me and let's have some dinner," I said, abandoning my trip for the dog. "I've got some trout in the shanty that I caught under the rocks in Little Falls brook this morning, and I bet they are a little better than any you ever pulled out of the Beaverkill."

"You're kiddin' me," said Scrammel.

I assured him that I was never more sincere in my life and I got up to start in the direction of Spruce Hut.

"What about that 'shang?" he asked. "Do I get that?"

"You can carry it for me," I replied, "provided you don't get it mixed up with your own. I don't yet admit that you have any right to it."

That settled the matter, that and the prospect of a square meal, for I suspect the fellow was actually hungry.

We tramped rapidly along with little to say on the way, and at last we found ourselves at my door. I unlocked it and told him to cut a little wood for the fire while I got the trout ready. He was but a few minutes getting his kindlings together, and he came in and laid them in the fireplace, ready to start with a match. As I was putting the fish in the pan he said to me, "Say, Mister—whatever your name is—let me cook them trout, will you? I know a thing or two about that that I don't believe you know."

I gave the man full charge of operations, and he went to work. I told him that no less an authority than Sir Isaac Walton had said that if a trout is not eaten within four or five hours after catching he is worth nothing, and I suggested that he had only some fifteen or twenty minutes in which to save the trout from the fate decreed by Sir Isaac.

Scrammel did not seem much worried, however, by the time limit, for he only said, "I never heard of Ike, but I'll bet he never saw a 'Beaverkiller' cook."

I could not gainsay this, so I kept silence and watched—and obeyed, for my guest called for several things that I would never have thought of using in cooking trout. Fortunately I was able to supply most of them.

His recipe if written out would be as indefinite as most of the recipes of natural cooks. It left a good deal to judgment. First, he slashed each trout three times on one side and laid them ready to put into the kettle. Then into the kettle he put equal amounts of vinegar, Catawba wine, water, and beer, which he said must be stale, but not too stale. Just the why of all this mixture I do not know, and I asked no questions, but produced the goods.

Just enough of the liquor was made to cover the fish, which were to be boiled!

Into it was put a generous supply of salt, also a slice or two of lemon and a pinch of grated horseradish with some savory and thyme, which I always keep in my "kitchen cupboard" in the little ounce packages just as they come from the drug store.

This preparation he set on a hot fire and let it boil up until it filled the kettle; then he put in the trout, one at a time. This last was, he volunteered, so that the fish would not cool the mixture enough to cause it to drop down flat. While the fish were boiling he took some of the mixture from the kettle and mixed it well with melted butter.

By the time he had completed his cooking he had the rest of the meal ready and he took the fish from the kettle, put them on a platter and poured his melted-butter mixture over them, adding some slices of lemon, and—oh, ye epicures! Not all the chefs of all the noteworthy lobster palaces could concoct anything that could be compared with this Beaverkiller's dish.

"Scrammel," said I, as we sat there devouring my trout, "the ginseng is yours, also half my kingdom. Where did you learn to do this?"

"It's a family trick that granny taught us. We don't know

much, us Scrammels, but we do know a thing or two pretty damn well."

"You certainly do," I returned, "and any time when you are coming this way my house here is open to you. If I'm not at home you'll find the key in a crack of the chimney outside. Whether your name is Scrammel, Smith, or Jones does not make any difference here."

"This is the first place I ever struck," he interjected, "where that was so. I'd like to get into a country some day where nobody knows who a Scrammel is. I'm gettin' tired o' some things."

"Scrammel," I answered "you are no different from other folks. Don't you suppose we all feel some days that we'd like to get where nobody knows anything about us? We'd be mighty glad to get back, though, because—I'll tell you a secret about everybody. The man who goes to a new place where he is Mister This or Mister That to everyone he meets gets to a point where he feels he absolutely *must* get back to where he is plain ordinary Bill or Joe. Don't you suppose the President in the White House feels some days that he'd give every cent his job is worth if he could just step out of it for a while and be a plain ordinary citizen that people could slap on the back and call 'Old Man' and do favors for without his feeling that they do it because they want something in return?"

"Say, I never thought of that," said my guest. "I'd hate to go where I didn't know anybody well enough to have 'em call me Nick. I'd rather be arrested once a month reg'lar for something I didn't do than to have to go 'round with a Mister tagged onto my name. That sure would be some Hell. You ain't told me your name?"

I told him.

"I don't want your 'shang," he said. "You're all to the good and I ain't got any more right to keep them roots than you have. Keep 'em."

I assured him that neither did I care for the ginseng, since I was not in the business and had simply dug it as a matter of pastime. I put the roots in his bag, and we parted with mutual respect: I for his ability to make of trout the most delicious morsels I ever ate, and he for my willingness to take a Scrammel home and make a temporary, and I'm not sure but a permanent, friend of him.

TREASURE HUNT *

When the old frame station of the Southern Central Railroad, later the Lehigh Valley, at Ensenore, New York, was torn down a few years ago, a neatly hand-lettered extract from the prose writings of Sir Edwin Arnold, the author of *The Light of Asia,* was removed from one wall:

> According to the Chinamen, Ginseng is the best and most potent of cordials, of stimulants, of tonics, of stomachics, cardiacs, febrifuges, and above all will renovate and reinvigorate failing forces. It fills the heart with hilarity, while its occasional use will, it is said, add a decade of years to ordinary human life. Can all these millions of Orientals, all these generations of men who have boiled Ginseng in silver kettles and have praised heaven for its many benefits, have been totally deceived?

This handsome testimonial, hung there by a station agent long since dead, was a memento of the ginseng craze that swept the Finger Lakes region in the latter part of the nineteenth century. Three of us Adams boys were in on the start of it. My cousins John and Sireno had come from Rochester to visit me and spend the summer vacation of 1884 in the rough camp my maternal grandfather rented from summer to summer at Second Peacock's Point, on Owasco Lake. Besides us, there were some eleven adults in the family group staying at the camp at the time. Shortly after my cousins' arrival, one of those furious gales that wrack the region blew up out of the northwest. For four days, no boat dared venture on the lake, and we were cut

* Samuel Hopkins Adams, "Treasure Hunt," from *Grandfather Stories,* New York, 1955.

off from Ensenore, our base of supplies, on the opposite shore.

Provisions ran low. This was nothing new; we had lived on the country before and could do so again. The grown-up males set out with guns and fishing-tackle to look for game and fish. A special mission was assigned to us boys. We were to bring in puffballs or, failing that, such other edible fungi as we could find. I was put in charge, as the one most familiar with fungi and the terrain.

A year before, a puffball four feet in circumference had been picked in Duryea's Woods, a mile upshore. I led my forces there in the hope of finding a repeater. Starting from the summit of the ninety-foot cliff that overhangs the lake, we deployed and scouted the forest back of it. At first, nothing rewarded us but some greasecups too small to be worth gathering, but as we emerged into a clearing, Reno shouted, and John and I ran to him. He was standing at a spot where two large basswoods had fallen and rotted, studying a plant some eighteen inches tall with leaves of a lucent green, as if they had been fresh-washed by rain. At the top of the plant was a queer-looking, half-formed cluster of pale berries.

"What kind of a dingus do you call that?" Reno asked.

"Don't touch it," I said. In a countryside rank with poison ivy and stinging nettle, the rule for anything unfamiliar was "Hands off."

"I bet it's some kind of sassafras," Reno said.

"Let's dig it up," said John.

I agreed, doubtfully, and Reno got out his new I.X.L. knife and set to work. The root was firmly set. It was a lumpy, unsightly object when, at last, it lay on the ground. There was an unwritten rule of the camp that any unusual object found in the woods should be reported or, if possible, brought back, so I broke off a hemlock branch and, protecting my hands with basswood leaves, managed to fasten the plant to it.

We then carried it in gingerly fashion out into the clearing. The ground here was dotted with pink-gills, the flavorsome and meaty field mushrooms. We filled our baskets, circled through the woods, and reached the Lower Lake Road. A two-seated, open wagon of the type called democrat wagon was coming toward us. The driver, a boy named Sid Selover, pulled up his span of farm horses and asked us what we had there.

"It's a plant we found in the woods," I said.

"Scared it'll bite you?" Sid asked.

"How do we know but what it's poisonous?" John said.

"Rats!" said Sid genially. "That's brightweed. Give you a dime for it.

"Where's your dime?" Reno challenged him.

"You wouldn't expect a fella to have it *on* him," Sid said.

"No trust, no bust," Reno retorted. "We'll keep it."

"Tell you what," Sid said. "Frank Clark, over to the Ensenore station, he'll buy it offen you."

"What's he want with it?" I asked.

"He sells it to the Chinese," Sid answered. "They make a powder of it and smoke it in their pipes and it drives 'em crazy." (Sid was a bit muddled, as we later learned.)

Back in camp, our pink-gills were received with approval. Uncle Woolsey had shot three rabbits and two squirrels. Uncle Jack had caught a mess of bullheads and one brown trout in Dutch Hollow Brook. My father, who had a gift for diplomacy, had talked a farm wife out of two loaves of bread and a dozen eggs at the exorbitant price of fifty cents, take it or leave it and she didn't care which, summer folk not being popular with the farmers.

The mysterious plant was examined and discussed by our elders, who thought it might be ginseng, and then again it might not. Frank Clark would know, they agreed, and they said we had better take it to him when the lake was navigable again.

The four-day gale blew itself out, and we boys rowed a mile and a half to consult Frank Clark. Being rather awed by him, I was not pleased when my cousins deputed to me the job of spokesman. Although not yet of age, Frank displayed a sort of pedagogical austerity. He had a pair of keen eyes set in a craggy and ascetic face. His loose-jointed form and shambling gait belied his considerable strength. He was the most feared batsman in the Owasco Lake Baseball League.

Frank already had a local reputation as a person of sagacity and authority. "Old head on young shoulders," the neighbors said of him. His taciturnity and abrupt manner were largely his defense against a time-wasting public, for he was a busy man. He was stationmaster of the Southern Central at Ensenore, as well as freight, express, and passenger agent, and telegraph operator, and postmaster. On the side, though in the station, he ran a general store. The station was Frank's inviolable castle. So jealous was he of his feudal rights and privileges that one Christmas Eve when he surprised a burglar who had been terrorizing the locality in the act of looting his till, his sense of outrage overcame his instinct of self-preservation. Unarmed, he strode up to the man and, with no more parley than a gruff "Gimme that gun," took away his .45, locked him in a closet, and stood guard until the early-morning train came in.

I approached this formidable person with respect and some misgiving. He was behind the post-office window, and I spoke to him through it. "Mr. Clark," I began, "we've got something—"

"I'm busy," said Mr. Clark.

"Shall we wait?" I asked.

"You needn't to," he said.

"When'll you be through?" I asked.

"Don't know. Stop pestering me."

John, a more resolute character than I, and not so familiar with Frank's reputation, took the stalk of the plant which I was dandling, and thrust it beneath the grille of the window. "All we want to know is, is this ginseng?" he asked boldly.

At the word, Frank set down the claw hammer with which he was opening a box, and drew the plant inside. "Come in," he snapped, jerking his head toward a door, and we went inside.

"Where did you find it?" he demanded.

"Duryea's Woods," I answered.

"Want to sell it?"

"Yes, sir."

"How much?"

Reno spoke up. "Sid Selover offered us a dime," he said.

Frank Clark carefully scraped the earth from a bump on the root and scratched its surface. We could smell a delicate and aromatic odor. "It's a good root," he said. "An old root. It'll fetch a price in New York." From his cash drawer he drew a shining object and held it up.

"A cartwheel!" Reno cried.

No less uplifted, I said, "Are you paying us a whole dollar for it?" and John muttered, "We'd have taken a quarter and said thank you."

Frank Clark said curtly, "I never cheated a customer yet, and I don't aim to start with you. Fetch me some more."

The interview was ended.

John and Reno and I promptly organized ourselves into the Gin Seng Tong, with oath and secret password. The valuable weed was by no means easy to find. It grew sparsely, often in difficult parts of the dangerously precipitous glens that cut through the lakeward slopes. But the sense of adventure, added to the profit motive, kept us at a high pitch of diligence.

Frank Clark told us he had a connection in New York with a reliable Chinatown exporter, who paid him a dollar and up for prime roots. In his dealings with us, he was scrupulously honest. He even laid aside his grouch to guide us on some of our expeditions. Well-shaded ground sloping to the east, we learned from him, was the likeliest place to find ginseng. The plants were hard to discern, during the early summer, in the thick undergrowth. In the fall, when the berries turned crimson, identification was easier. For the present, our cicerone told us, he would accept only well-grown plants. The next year, he intended to start his own nursery, and then any stalk that could be transplanted would do.

The Gin Seng Tong had a good season. There was no week in which we did not make half a dozen marketable finds, and by the end of the summer our treasury fund had reached an incredible twenty-odd dollars.

That autumn, after we boys had gone home to Rochester, a dire event befell. Ike Jump's nephew, an ignoramus who lived outside Ensenore and didn't know ginseng from skunk cabbage, chanced upon a well-aged ginseng plant in Ensenore

Glen, where he was searching for a lost sow. The plant's root was of human form, with branching arms and legs and a spindly, headless neck—a perfect specimen of a rare type. Frank Clark, to whom the boy took it, had heard of these "mandragons" and knew that they commanded a fancy price from the Chinese, who attributed to them desirable potencies beyond those of the usual root. He made a special shipment of this one to his New York correspondent and, when the payment came, handed over to the lucky finder a ten-dollar bill, which made his eyes pop.

Unfortunately, the boy bragged. Probably he lied. Rumor buzzed. The root had fetched a fabulous amount in Chinatown. Fifty dollars, said some. Nonsense, said others, not fifty, seventy-five. One hundred. One hundred and fifty. Two hundred. Two hundred and fifty. The sum was whatever came into the gossipmonger's head, but on one point the whole region was soon agreed: there were fortunes to be had in the woods. Everybody fell to root-grubbing. The ginseng craze was on, and only snowfall put a stop to it.

None of this, however, reached the ears of us three tong members, impatiently at school in Rochester. Out of our summer's earnings we bought two spades, a mattock, and a botany book, but it was the next July before we at last got back to Second Peacock's.

A scene of devastation awaited us. The countryside had been ravaged. Botanizing vandals from Auburn, Moravia, and even distant Syracuse had scarified the tender face of the earth. Nothing was spared. The demented prowlers had yanked out by the roots such innocent and useless vegetation as burdock, elderberry, tansy, joe-pye weed, mandrake, oxheart, and pokeberry, and the furor still raged. The station platform at Ensenore was littered each day with plants, most of them trash, which Frank Clark had to burn.

New excitement was stimulated by a report from Skaneateles—a summer renter had found in his teasel field a mandragon root three feet long. It later turned out to be a counterfeit as gross as the neighboring and previous Cardiff giant, and we heard that the Skaneateles Chinaman to whom its sculptor had submitted it for verification chased the man out of his laundry at the point of a flatiron.

But enough authentic finds of ginseng—"shang" to the trade—were made to keep the pitch of interest high, a two- or three-dollar specimen being not infrequent. The farmers caught the craze. They posted their woods and even stood guard at night with shotguns. Old Man Beardsley, over near Henpeck—a name now, alas!, deleted from local nomenclature—attracted some attention with a sign that read,

ALL PERSONS ARE POSITIVELY FORBIDDEN
TO VEGETATE ON THESE PREMISSES

His wood lot was worth guarding. It yielded enough plants to let him start quite a respectable nursery.

Many others decided to go in for ginseng culture, and for a time little close-planted plots enriched with leaf mold and covered with roofs of laths three inches apart, in the prescribed fashion, became a familiar sight.

All this competition, and especially the posting, made the going tough for the Adams tong. How many copses and groves we were ignominiously chased from, I would not undertake to say. Where we were able to explore unmolested, others had been before us. The leavings were always meagre—a few scrawny stalks with spindling roots worth only a few cents. Our total takings in a month of woodmanship that would have taxed the endurance of Daniel Boone were under three dollars. The game was up. Our tong disbanded. We traded our botany book for a dime novel and our tools for fishing tackle, and turned our attention to the perch in Owasco Lake.

For the most part, the farmers had spoiled our sport and our prospect of becoming botanical millionaires without doing themselves much good. Lack of scientific knowledge was their trouble; ginseng culture is not a hit-or-miss activity. Few of the cultivators knew how to protect their crops. Blight, root rot, and mildew attacked the plants. Snails and eelworms preyed upon them. After a few years of this, most of the experimenters gave up.

More patient growers, however, became expert and did a

profitable business. Williard R. Austin, of Moravia, who once found a wild root weighing an even pound, and his fellow-Moravians, the Bowens, father and son, stuck to the trade for more than twenty years, marketing their product in Elmira and New York, for export to China. There was little demand for it in this country, though a patent-medicine stomachic called Garfield Tea was based upon ginseng. However, as these successful ginseng gardens expanded, a new risk developed. Professional night raiders from New York appeared upon the scene.

Frank Clark was a victim of these. Learning of raids on Seneca Lake, he fenced his patch with barbed wire and hung the wire with bells of loud tone and high sensitivity. He had not reckoned with wild creatures accustomed to wander at night. The belled wires proved disastrously responsive to their visits. A dozen times a night, poor Frank, roused by the clangor, would leap from his bed, seize his shotgun, and charge down the hills to his ginseng patch in time to see a rabbit scurry into the brush or a raccoon swarm up a tree trunk. Once, there was a wild carillon when a deer blundered into the wire. Frank shot the deer, which was some satisfaction to him.

Sturdy though Frank was, the strain told upon him. He lost ten pounds through lack of sleep. He discarded the bells and kept a dog tied inside the enclosure. But the dog had friends in the vicinity; it learned to slip its leash and crawl through the wire, causing Frank more sleeplessness. In the course of time, it died. Its owner did not replace it, since the depredations of the ginseng bandits had flagged. Several seasons went by without any local thefts. Then, one December morning, Frank went out to find his plot ravished. There were broad wagon-tire marks in the soft roadway. Frank followed the trail as far as Cascade, at the head of the lake, but lost it there. Nearly twelve hundred dollars' worth of root had been dug up. Frank quit the ginseng business in disgust.

There was encouragement for those who stuck to the ginseng trade in the steady rise in price. In the days of the Adams tong, average roots brought no more than two dollars a pound.

By 1900, the price was six dollars and a half. In 1927, there was a shortage in the Orient, and the price reached a fabulous high of twenty-four dollars, but by that time the industry had been all but abandoned in the lakes district. Cultivated plants brought much less than the wild growth, the latter being credited with more powerful medicinal effects, and the forests had been pretty well denuded.

"The shang rustlers had got smart," says octogenarian Arthur J. Bowen, of Moravia. "They'd learned to wait till fall, when the berries turn bright red and you can spot a plant ten rods away through the shrubbery. Nowadays, I couldn't take you to a wild shang plant if I wanted to."

Mr. Bowen is the author of a poetic lament for the ravaged woodlands of his prime, entitled "Extermination" and copyrighted in 1903:

> The big forests with their timbers so tall
> Is where the Ginseng grew, both large and small:
> But soon came the men at a terrible rate
> And cleaned up the forest—which is the Ginseng's fate.
> But now the shang digger with his eye so keen
> Has hunted the woods, and there is not a plant to be seen.

The horticultural authorities at Cornell University confirm Mr. Bowen's pessimism, though they believe that the species is not wholly extinct in the Finger Lakes region. Certainly, however, it is very rare. It has not recovered from the pillage of the frenzied amateurs of the last century. Yet I never drive through the autumn woods that border my home on the shore of Owasco Lake without keeping an instinctively hopeful eye out for a glint of crimson topping a leafy green shaft. I cannot help feeling that I might chance upon a full-grown plant and exhume from beneath it that valuable symbolic vegetable and promoter of virility, a seven-year mandragon root.

Wild Ginseng
...FOR SALE...

We Ship Direct from Diggers to Parties Desiring to Start Gardens

Orders booked as received and filled in order of filing after August 20th. Prices on application.

Reference, Bank of Cumberland Gap.

CEDRO CO., CUMBERLAND GAP, TENNESSEE

FOR SALE
Northern Ohio and N. Y. Wild Roots

Also a few thousand New York cultivated two-year old Roots; can furnish a limited amount of 1902 Seed, and am now booking orders for large or small lots of 1903 Seed. I guarantee every root and seed to be northern and the true North American variety. I furnished many customers last year with roots and seeds, with uniform satisfaction to all. Write me for prices.

J. C. SELBY, CLYDE, OHIO.

GINSENG SEED AND ROOTS

WE offer a limited quantity of one, two and three-year old ginseng ROOTS and of ginseng SEED for sale at reasonable prices. Every root and seed sold from our gardens is *guaranteed to be pure and genuine American ginseng*. We have three different plantations, embracing almost an acre of growing ginseng. All our plants are of the third generation of prime, cultivated American ginseng. The seed we sell will be from the fourth generation of cultivated plants.

☞ A discount of 15 per cent. will be allowed on all orders received by us on or before August 25, 1903.

For prices and information address

Illinois Stock and Plant Company Springfield, Illinois.

Eureka Ginseng Garden

I have the following stock for sale:

100,000 1902 Seed, **$16** per **1000.** I expect to have 600,000 1903 crop; will sell 300,000 at **$10** per **1000.** 50,000 one-year old Cultivated Ginseng Roots at **$7.50** per **100.** 100,000 Northern Ohio Wild Roots; first size, averaging two years old, **$45** per **1000**; from 1/4 to 1/2 in. in diameter, **$80** per **1000**; larger than 1/2 in., **$100** per **1000.**

I guarantee every Root and Seed I sell to be genuine North American Ginseng, and first-class in every respect.

J. L. TODD, MAPLETON, OHIO.

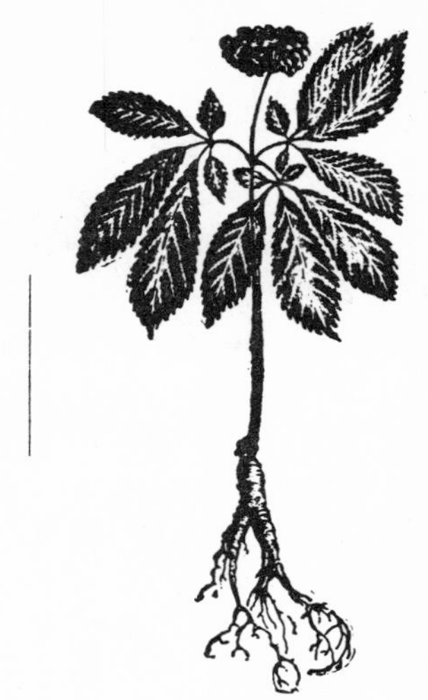

We Have for Sale

1902 ginseng seed raised in Central New York from first-class North American ginseng. A few thousand two-year old cultivated roots. Several thousand wild roots which have been under cultivation two years; these have had good care and are fine roots.

We also have under contract several experienced ginseng diggers, and expect to be able to place on the market 50,000 first-class wild roots, all northern dug, which will be sold at a reasonable price.

Both members of this company are also members of the New York State Ginseng Growers' Association, and in good standing.

We have also issued an illustrated copyright book on the cultivation of ginseng, written entirely from observation and experience, giving a short history of ginseng, showing the best kind of soil needed for its cultivation, preparation of beds, planting of seed and roots, enclosure and covering, harvesting seeds and roots, marketing your product, etc. Price of book, 25c.

Reference: First National Bank, Tully, N. Y.

Tully Ginseng Co.,

TULLY, N. Y.

Ginseng

GET ALL YOU CAN FOR YOUR ROOTS

We Pay the Utmost

WE WANT LARGE QUANTITIES OF

Cultivated, Transplanted and Wild Roots

also Culls and Fibre

Send your lots and receive my best offer, or if you don't care to ship the lot, send a good sized sample of two to five pounds which fairly represents the lot.

Satisfactory Returns Guaranteed

Our offers are held open a reasonable length of time.

References—The Greenwich Bank, Broadway and 18th Sts., New York; Duns and Bradstreets Agencies.

BENJAMIN DORMAN

147 West 24th Street, New York, N. Y.

From the advertising section of *Special Crops,* a magazine for ginseng growers. The high prices offered by the New York exporting houses were not lies, but there was not, by the beginning of this century, enough wild root for everyone who wanted to make a living by gathering it. And most ginseng farms failed.

Some Advice

As we have seen, ginseng has been known in the West for centuries, but its current widespread use can be attributed to the changes that occurred in Western society in the 1960s, changes one could briefly describe as a turning outward of nearly a whole generation's perception to new forms of meaningful experience, whether from the East or from our own heritage, now seen as richly multifarious.

We have retained some habits, in spite of this new awareness. They are concerned mostly with consuming, perhaps more specifically with getting our money's worth. A great many people are paying a lot for Asiatic ginseng these days—ordinary Korean white root now sells for as much as ten dollars an ounce—and they are taking doses of it for many purposes other than primarily curative—tonic, carminative, restorative, rejuvenescent, even aphrodisiac. And so here are a few words of advice.

Unless you are used to ginseng and have taken it over a long period of time, buying expensive grades of root is probably only a waste of money. If someone were at death's door, perhaps only the best Imperial wild root would do. (Actually I believe it's unobtainable, though certain distributors on the West Coast claim to be able to supply it.) For more ordinary purposes use the least expensive root of good quality you can find.

Ginseng is a subtle medicine: not that its effects are not perceptible, but one becomes aware of them gradually. Everybody wants to know if ginseng makes you high. Decidedly yes, but as with other gifts from the East to contemporary Western culture (yoga, *t'ai chi,* transcendental meditation) it takes time for the body to get the message and let you know it. Of course, since ginseng promotes a change in metabolism and body chemistry—the change is a chemical one, and clinically perceptible—one would expect its effects to be comparatively quickly felt. In general, if taken wisely, a regimen of ginseng will make you conscious of a marked improvement in your well-being within about a month. Your body will probably be more resistant to sore throats and nasal congestion; if you catch colds easily that will happen less frequently. Bodily functions may be regulated; prolonged work will be easier to accomplish. Ginseng gives stamina, a quality not to be confused with willpower, but perhaps ancillary to it.

Taken wisely—this is the key to success with the root. The problem is partly—as the Chinese opinion, reported by Fr. Huc (p. 190), would have it—that Westerners' constitutions, being already comparatively hot, do not respond well to a heating drug such as ginseng. Certainly we do not increase our receptiveness to ginseng's effects by our widespread cultural reliance upon stimulants. Most people who take them regularly regard coffee, tea, cannabis, tobacco, alcohol as steadying or even calming in their effects, even though their physiological actions are just the opposite. Basically, they make it hard for ginseng to do its work, confusing the body by making contrary or incompatible demands on it. Many would consider it a radical or difficult experiment, but the best way to start with ginseng is to take it for a month as a substitute for whatever stimulants you have been using. There is almost no doubt that your health and bodily tone will undergo a considerable improvement in those four weeks, and that should provide reason enough to continue to take ginseng in the same way.

The best way to prepare ginseng for taking is probably to make a simple elixir. Place an ounce of root in a glass or porcelain container (not metal, enamel, or porous earthenware) and add to it a pint of spirits—high-proof vodka is probably best to use, because it has the least taste. Let stand in a warm place overnight. Then each morning upon arising take a tablespoonful of the elixir, again using only a glass or porcelain spoon. When the elixir is used up, add another pint of spirits to the root and use this secondary elixir in the same way as the first. When that is gone, throw the roots away. Alcohol is a good vehicle for ginseng, because it dissolves all the root's essential oils and preserves them far better than water. If the idea of vodka seems disgusting, try dark rum, as in Dr. Henry's recipe (pp. 189–190), which provided the American pioneers with a staple tonic.

Bibliography

Here, arranged in roughly chronological order, is a compilation of knowledge about ginseng, its history, cultivation, and medical properties, stories and accounts of people who seek it and use it. Quotations from the works listed and descriptions of their authors are included wherever appropriate.

This is not an exhaustive list: popular magazine articles, growers' and government publications, specialized research, with a few significant exceptions, have been left out. What seems important here is the lore: beliefs and truths (the two sometimes overlap, but not always) that draw people to ginseng, the popular basis for the miraculous claims that have always been made about it. If there is one thing a book of lore can show, it is that people learn from one another, just as authors borrow from one another, discriminately: it is rare that a complete lie survives undetected through many generations. Whatever has been claimed for a long time about ginseng that seems unbelievable to many Western ears very likely has some part of truth to it. In particular, the supercilious tone of many of the Western commentators should not be taken too seriously. Men of the West have always believed that all alien cultures they ever encountered, and especially the (non-Christian) beliefs of the people, were greatly inferior to their own. But why always look for utter objectivity? Truth can be found and told by the prejudiced, and that is often the case in the pages that follow.

Khordadbeh (ninth-century Arab geographer). *Book of Roads and Provinces,* quoted by W. E. Griffis, *Corea, the Hermit Nation,* New York (7th ed.), 1904, p. 2.

> What lies on the other side of China is unknown land. But high mountains rise up densely across from Kantu [Shantung]. These lie over in the land of Silla [a corruption of Shinra, the predominant state in Korea in Khordadbeh's time], which is rich in gold. Moslems who visit this country often allow themselves, through the advantages of the gold, to be induced to settle here.

They export from thence ginseng, deerhorn, aloes, camphor, nails, saddles, porcelain, satin, zimmit [cinnamon?], and galanga [ginger?].

Semmedo, Alvaro. *Relatione della grande monarchia della Cina.* (G. B. Grattini, trans.) Rome, 1643, p. 31.

[This book, written in 1633, contains the earliest published mention of ginseng in Europe.]

In the province of Leaotung a root is produced which is sold at the price of double its weight in silver. It is a marvelous medicine, which is able to increase the strength of the frame and to restore the exhausted animal powers. The Chinese call it *Gin sem.*

Martini, Martinus. *Bellum Tartaricum, or the Conquest of the Great and most renowned Empire of China, By the Invasion of the Tartars, who in these last seven years, have wholly subdued that vast Empire . . . now faithfully Translated into English.* London, 1654, p. 9.

These Tartars every year, either as Subjects or Friends, came into China by the Province of Leaotung to traffick with the Inhabitants; for, being brought to poverty and misery, they thought no more of making war against China. The Merchandise they brought were several, as the root called Ginsem, so much esteemed amongst the Chineses, and all sorts of pretious skins, as those of Castor, Martais & Zibellens, and also Horse-hair, of which the Chinese make their Nets, and the men, though madly, use it in tying up their hair, as the handsomest dress they can appear in. But those Tartars multiplyed so fast, as they grew quickly into seven Governments which they called Hordes, as much as to say into seven Lordships, and these fighting one against another, at length about the year of Christ MDL, came to erect a Kingdom, which they called the Kingdom of Niuche.

———. *Novus Atlas Sinensis.* Amsterdam, 1655, p. 44.

[The earliest description in a European book of the medicinal effects of ginseng.]

When one chews [ginseng], it is disagreeable, because of a sweetness mixed with a little bitterness: it greatly increases the vital spirits, to such a degree that the dose needs to be barely two scruples [about a twelfth of an ounce]. If one takes a little more, it will cause exhausted strength to return, and set up an agreeable heat in the body . . . Those of a more robust or heated constitution will put their life in danger if they use it, because of the increasing and exciting of the spirits; but it works miracles for the feeble and worn out, and for those whose strength has been exhausted by a long illness or some other accident. It restores vital spirits to the dying to such an extent that they often have the time to employ other remedies and recover their health. The Chinese report marvelous things of the root; for a pound of it they will give three of silver.

Kircher, Athanasius. *La Chine, illustrée de plusieurs monuments, tant sacrés que profanes, et de quantité de recherchés de la nature et de l'art.* (F. S. Dalquié, trans.) Amsterdam, 1670, p. 241.
[Kircher visited China extensively, but apparently never saw ginseng in use. He recounts its reputation for "giving immortality to those who eat it," and in this place quotes extensively from Fr. Martini's *Novus Atlas Sinensis* (q.v.).]

Ray, John. *Historia Plantarum.* 3 vols. London, 1686–1704. Vol. 2 (1688), p. 1338.
[Ray was the greatest pre-Linnæan English botanist, and his research into plant lore was thorough and generally authoritative.]

Book XXIII: on anomalous plants; Chapter XX: The Ninzin Root, otherwise known as ginseng and gensing.

In truth no other substance, it is said, will cure the body of all languors and illnesses, and not only this, but will even act for those who will take it regularly as a preservative against the effects of evils and poisons. Those about to expire have testified that upon chewing the root their spirits are restored and their hearts are refreshed.

Lecompte, Louis-Daniel. *Memoirs and Remarks . . . made in above Ten Years Travel through the Empire of China . . . A New Translation of the best Paris Edition.* London, 1738, pp. 226–227.
[Lecompte was a Jesuit. His voyages in China were made in the 1690s and his well-known *Memoirs,* containing a great deal of superciliousness and inaccuracy, were extensively reprinted, translated, and used by later commentators.]

Take a drachm [one-eighth ounce] of this root (you must begin with a little dose, and may increase it afterwards, according to the effect the former doses shall produce) dry it before the fire in a paper, or infuse it in wine, till it be sated by it; then cut it in little pieces with your teeth (and not with a knife, iron diminishing its virtue) and, when it is calcined, take the powder in form of a bolus, in warm water or wine, according as your distemper will permit. This will be an excellent cordial, and by continuing it you will find yourself sensibly fortified.

Sarrasin, Michel. "Sur le Gin-seng." *Histoire de l'Académie royale des sciences* [for the year 1718]. Paris, 1719, pp. 41–45.
[An account of the discovery of ginseng by the Frenchmen Jartoux and Lafitau (qq.v.) in China and North America respectively.]

Bartram, John. *Observations on the Inhabitants, Climate, Soil, Rivers, Productions, Animals, and other matters worthy of Notice, made by Mr. John Bartram in his Travels from Pensilvania to Onondago, Oswego and the Lake Ontario in Canada.* London, 1751, *passim.*
[Bartram was a great observer, and always mentioned the presence and abundance of ginseng whenever he found it.]

> We entered the vale at 5 [o'clock], then crossed a run and rode along a rich level for several miles, and under the delightful protection of very tall trees that brought us to a creek, a branch of the Susquehanah, where we lodged surrounded by ginseng. [p. 64]

Kalm, Peter. *Travels into North America.* (J. R. Forster trans. from *En Resa til Norra America,* Stockholm, 1753.) 2 vols. London, 1770, vol. 2, p. 131.

[Per Kalm was a competent naturalist, a kind of universal scientist, and an acute observer, sent to North America by Linnæus in 1749 to study the plants.]

> August 7th [1749]: [Ginseng] is not everywhere very common, for sometimes you may search the woods for the space of several miles without finding a single plant of it; but in those spots where it grows it is always found in great abundance. It flowers in May and June, and its berries are ripe at the end of August. It bears transplanting very well, and will soon thrive in its new ground. Some people here, who have gathered the berries, and put them into their kitchen-gardens, told me they lay one or two years in the ground without coming up . . . The French use this root for curing the asthma, as a stomachic, and to promote fertility in women . . . During my stay in Canada, all the merchants in Quebec and Montreal received orders from their correspondents in France to send over a quantity of ginseng, there being an uncommon demand for it this summer. The roots were accordingly collected in Canada with all possible diligence; the Indians especially travelled about the country in order to collect as much as they could together, and to sell it to the merchants at Montreal . . . Many people feared lest by continuing for several successive years to collect these plants without leaving one or two in each place to propagate their species, there will soon be very few of them left; which I think is very likely to happen, for by all accounts they formerly grew in abundance round Montreal, but at present there is not a single plant of it to be found, so effectually have they been rooted out.

"Urban" in *The Gentleman's Magazine.* London, May, 1753, p. 209b.

[This magazine, like some in our own day, was a widely read source of interesting information for many people who wanted to be up-to-date with discoveries, trends, and current opinions, but who, for the most part, rarely read anything else.]

> A root, of which the Chinese have long been extravagantly fond, has of late, I find, been recommended in this place [London]; and merits the greater consideration, as it is one of the products of our own colonies in North America. The name of this drug, is Ginseng; . . . some considerable parcels of the root have been sent to China, and disposed of to great advantage; the advantage would still have been greater, had those who gather the root, col-

lected it at a proper season, and cured it in the Chinese manner. It has been tried in many cases here, yet not so fully as to establish its character in any particular disease. In tedious, chronick coughs, incident to people in years, a decoction of it has been of service: and in such disorders as attend advancing years, where the solids are too inactive, the fluids viscid, and acrimonious, it seems to promise considerable benefit, if used in moderate doses, and long continued. Time will perhaps discover its proper effects, and as it consists of a mild, lubricating mucilage, joined with some degree of aromatick warmth, it may be tryd in such disorders with great safety. One drachm and a half boiled in four ounces of water in a close vessel, and slow heat, about half an hour, will be a proper mean dose; or it may be given in powder to half a drachm or two scruples. Upon the whole, tho' it does not seem entitled to even a moderate share of those virtues that are romanticky ascribed to it by the Chinese, yet it is very well worthy the attention of the faculty, and promises fair to be a more useful and efficacious medicine, than many now kept in the shops.

Michaux, F. A. *Travels to the Westward of the Allegheny Mountains in the States of Ohio, Kentucky and Tennessee,* &c. (B. Lambert, trans.) London, 1805, pp. 207–212.

Although the ginseng is not a plant peculiar to Kentucky, it is, however, very abundant in it, which has determined me to notice it here . . . It thrives most in the mountainous regions of the Alleghenys, where it is more abundant as the mountains lie further to the south-west. It is also met with in the environs of New-York and Philadelphia, as well as in those parts of the northern states situated between the mountains and the sea; but it is so scarce as not to be worth the trouble of seeking. A man will not be able to take up more than eight or nine pounds of the fresh roots, in a day . . . For a short time after its discovery here, this root was sold for its weight in gold: but this advantageous commerce was not of long duration. The ginseng exported from America was so ill prepared, that it fell to a very low price, and the trade ceased almost wholly: however, it has begun to grow better for some time. If the Americans have been so long deprived of this lucrative trade, it must be ascribed to the little care they take in collecting and preparing the ginseng.

Henry, Samuel. *New and Complete American Family Herbal, wherein, is displayed the true properties and medical virtues of the plants, indigenous to the United States of America.* 1st ed. New York, 1814, p. 139.

[Samuel Henry's was one of the most popular herbals ever published, and went through dozens of editions throughout the nineteenth century.]

Take one pound of the fresh [ginseng] roots cut small, put them in a gallon of old Jamaica spirits [dark rum], and let it stand in the sun for two weeks, every now and then shaking the vessel. In all weaknesses from excess in venery, pain in the bones from colds, and gravelly complaints, let the patient take a wine glass of this tincture three times a day, on an empty stomach. I know a man in New-Jersey, who was so debilitated and afflicted with pains in his bones, that he expected nothing but death every day, who by taking the ginseng in rum was able to follow his business on the farm, and his pains entirely removed in a few days.

Klaproth, J. *Chrestomathie mandchou, ou receuil de textes mandchoux, destiné aux personnes qui veulent s'occuper de l'étude de cette langue.* Paris, 1828, p. 255.

[This extract is from the "Eulogy to the city of Mukden" by the Emperor Khien Lung, November 2, 1748. This famous eulogy, composed in Chinese and Manchu, has always been considered in China a model of elevated style.]

As to plants, the one which is called orkhota [ginseng] always puts forth three stems, on which the leaves always appear in fives; undoubtedly the plant absorbs the wonderful breath of the country, and becomes infused with its precious worth.

Thompson, Zadoch. *History of Vermont, natural, civil, and statistical.* Burlington, 1842, part 1, p. 221.

The Ginseng, *Panax quinquefolia,* was the first medicinal root which attracted much attention in this state, and is the only one which has been to any considerable extent an article of exportation . . . Upon the settlement of this state the ginseng was found to grow there in great plenty and perfection, and it soon began to be sought with eagerness for exportation. For many years it was purchased at nearly all the retail stores in the state, and was sent to seaports to be shipped to China.

Huc, Evariste-Régis. *Travels in Tartary, Thibet, and China, during the Years 1844–5–6.* (W. Hazlitt, trans.) 2 vols. London, 1852, vol. 1, p. 106.

[Huc was a missionary, traveled extensively in China, but got most of his information on ginseng from accounts of earlier voyagers.]

The nature of ginseng is too heating, the Chinese physicians admit, for the European temperament, already, in their opinion, too hot. The price is enormous, and doubtless its dearness contributes, with a people like the Chinese, to raise its celebrity so high. The rich and the Mandarins probably use it only because it is above the reach of other people, and out of pure ostentation.

Wilson, John. *Medical Notes on China.* London, 1846, p. 256.

[John Wilson practiced medicine in the English colony in Shanghai for fifteen years in the first part of the nineteenth century.]

> No one's case need be considered desperate, who can procure [ginseng], the *pabulum vitæ,* in abundance; but it is so costly, as to be beyond the reach of the great proportion of the afflicted. Generally it is, except in very small quantities, an article of sale by itself, the man who deals it dealing in nothing else; and it cannot be procured in every drug shop. At Tinghae, the writer visited a ginseng repository, which was a most unpromising and barren-looking place. The commodity is too precious to be displayed at windows, or deposited on shelves. Strong-boxes behind a rampart of counters alone appear; there it is rigidly kept, disposed in small cases, each of which contains about a drachm weight. A stranger well introduced, or a person of known character, may look at, but not touch, it, till he has paid the price. Proverbially it is represented as worth more than its weight in gold, which is confirmed by common practice; for the dealer alluded to asked, as a matter of course, for a bit shown, at the rate of twenty-four dollars an ounce.

Lockhart, William. *The Medical Missionary in China: A Narrative of Twenty Years' Experience*. London, 1861, pp. 108–110.

> Presents of this root are frequently made; and accompanying the medicine is usually sent a small, beautifully-finished double kettle, in which the ginseng is prepared as follows. The inner kettle is made of silver, and between this and the outside vessel, which is a copper jacket, is a small space for holding water. The silver kettle, which fits on a ring near the top of the outer covering, has a cup-like cover, in which rice is placed, with a little water; the ginseng with water in the inner vessel; a cover placed over all, and the apparatus put on the fire. When the rice in the cover is sufficiently cooked, the medicine is ready, and is then eaten by the patient, who drinks the ginseng tea at the same time.
>
> A ginseng merchant of my acquaintance, who had a small office at a goldsmith's shop, near the great east gate of Shanghai, has often exhibited to me his stock of the valuable root. He was a man of literary tastes and ability, and by profession a physician, but gave his whole attention to the sale of this article; his entire stock of which was contained in two strong boxes. When I have called to see him, he would first order tea, and after a little time spent over this in general conversation, would ask if "I wished to see his stock of the root?" On [my] replying in the affirmative, he deliberately fetched his keys, and calling an attendant to shut the door, so that neither strangers from the outer shop, nor damp air, might enter his clean and beautifully-furnished sanctum, which was also thoroughly dry, proceeded slowly to unlock the boxes. Opening the outer box, he removed several paper parcels, which appeared to fill the box, but under them was a second box (or perhaps two small boxes)

which, when taken out, showed the bottom of the large box, and all the intervening space, occupied with more paper parcels. These parcels, he said, "contain quicklime, for the purpose of absorbing any moisture, and keeping the boxes quite dry;" the lime being packed in paper for the sake of cleanliness. The smaller box, which held the ginseng, was lined with thin sheet lead; the ginseng, further enclosed in silk wrappers, was kept in little silken-covered boxes. At last after opening many receptacles, the actual medicine was displayed, each root sewn with silk to its silken wrapper. Taking up a piece, and requesting his visitor not to breathe upon it, nor handle it, he would dilate upon the many merits of the drug, and the numerous cures it had effected. The cover of the root, according to its value, was silk, either embroidered or plain; cotton cloth, or paper. Some of the root was worth not more than six to twelve dollars an ounce; other portions rose in price, to the most expensive, which was of the enormous value of 300 and even 400 dollars an ounce. This latter the merchant prized of course very highly, and allowed only a glance at it, as he said "it might be injured by exposure to the air." The inspection finished, each root was carefully returned to its place in the box, and this to its position on the lime; the parcels of the latter were readjusted, the outer box locked; and my friend, with a look of relief, would sit down and continue his conversation.

This man, who had a great repute for exceedingly good ginseng, was well known by the common dealers, who regarded him as an authority in his line of business. When asked as to the amount of his trade, he replied that he sold a good deal of the commoner kinds; and every now and then a little of the higher-priced article to government officers and wealthy persons, who gave it to their wives when pregnant, supposing that it marvelously purified the blood and invigorated the system. Another cup of tea, and thanks for the courtesy, would close the interview.

I occasionally took visitors to this merchant's little office, to see his mode of business, and more especially to see himself, as a good specimen of the rich, and quiet, and respectable Chinese tradesman—not eager for crowding customers, but depending on his reputation for the sale of his goods.

Hanbury, Daniel. *Science Papers, chiefly Pharmacological and Botanical.* (Joseph Ince, ed.) London, 1876, p. 261.

[Hanbury spent some time as a physician in China, and mentions ginseng here, adding some misinformation about the varieties most valued.]

Speer, William. *The Oldest and the Newest Empire: China and the United States.* Pittsburgh, 1877, p. 61.

In Manchuria, the country from which they originally came,

the emperors are buried. Kirin is to the eastward of Moukden, and borders on Corea. Here the famous wild plant, ginseng . . . is gathered as an exclusive monopoly of the emperor. Ginseng was then discovered in New England . . . and in 1752 the celebrated Rev. Jonathan Edwards complains in a letter to his friend, the Rev. Mr. McCulloch in Scotland, that since it had been found the previous summer in the woods about Stockbridge and elsewhere in New England, and in the country of the Six Nations, "the traders in Albany have been eager to purchase all they could of the root to send to England, where they make great profit by it. This has occasioned our Indians of all sorts, young and old, to spend abundance of time in the woods, and sometimes to a great distance, in the neglect of public worship and their husbandry, and also in going much to Albany to sell their roots (which proves worse to them than going into the woods), where they are always much in the way of temptation and drunkenness." This was probably the first of the troubles arising out of commercial intercourse between China and America. The East India Company sold the ginseng in China at a profit of five or six hundred per cent. The trade in it yet continues. Large quantities are annually sent to China from the newer parts of the West, especially from Minnesota and Wisconsin, which correspond somewhat in climate with the districts where it is found in Manchuria and Corea.

Bretschneider, Emil. *Botanicon Sinicum: Notes on Chinese Botany from Native and Western Sources.* London, 1882, pp. 29–30.

[Bretschneider spent a lifetime on Chinese botany, mainly in China. He knew all the plants and herbals, and the names, old and new, for practically every one of the thousands of drugs used in China.]

Ginseng is listed first among the *kün,* or sovereign drugs, in the *Pen king* [a very ancient Chinese work of materia medica], which says of these drugs, "They support human life, and thereby resemble Heaven." Following ginseng on the list are orange, slippery elm, mushrooms, liquorice, cannabis. "Whatever quantity you take of these, or howsoever long you use them, they are harmless." There are three lists of the *kün,* 365 drugs in all.

Macintyre, the Rev. John. "Roadside Religion in Manchuria." *Journal of the China Branch of the Royal Asiatic Society.* Vol. 21 (1886), pp. 45–46.

The objects worshipped in these roadside shrines I found more numerous than I had anticipated. I examined from twenty to thirty a day for a period of five weeks, and had much help besides from a Chinaman who was able to overtake many which lay at a considerable distance from our line of route. I shall begin with the more familiar ones, which are indeed more or less common throughout the Empire. The Three Holy Ones have perhaps the first claim upon our attention, though in the greater part of the route it is a tie between them and the Fox and Stoat . . . The leader of all is The Spirit of the Hills. He is chief of the Three, and he has a recognized place in the other groups. Where there is a picture he is sketched as a terrible looking fellow, with a black face, and with an axe over his shoulder. In one of the city temples I once saw quite an artistic representation of lions in clay, where, in addition to the axe symbol, he had on his left a crouching tiger, and on his right a bear. At another time, on a bold peak dominating one of our wildest mountain passes there was a tastefully executed granite slab with an inscription to the effect that the treasures of the hills are in his keeping. This gives us his character and functions. He is the officer of Woods and Forests. It is his to reveal the treasures hidden there and to grant protection from the ravages of wild beasts. I have heard alike from Coreans and Chinese that they pray to him when searching for ginseng and other such precious herbs; and one sees ample evidence on hill and plain that the fear of wild animals is upon all. Nay, in some districts it was the tiger himself was worshipped as the Divinity. "Shoot him?" said one to me, "We have not the weapons for one thing; and then is he not the divinity of the hills?" I used to think the Chinaman contrasted favorably with the ancient Egyptian in his sound horror to anything approaching to animal worship. Yet in many a lonely spot one hears tiger and bear, and fox and stoat—and serpent too—personified in the most deliberate manner. They have their personal traits, their idiosyncrasies, their foible; and one forgets altogether the forester with his axe and attendant tiger, and thinks of the animals themselves as independent beings whose strength, cruelty, craftiness and like qualities hold the simple mountaineer in constant awe. Yet it is of the essence of religion in China that the forester should be king and not the tiger, and that, while it is a human form which is presented to the eye, it is a spirit which is worshipped.

Stanton, G. "The Cultivation of Ginseng." *Garden and Forest*. Vol. 5 (1892), p. 223.

There was a touch of pathos in a remark I heard from a farmer's wife while rambling over the hills of Cortland County, New York, in quest of Ginseng. "It is a shame," said she, "that Ginseng is so hunted and stolen from our forests that we can hardly find a root for our own use." From Minnesota to Carolina the gathering has been carried on until in the places where this beautiful plant was once so abundant that one could hardly step without treading on it, only single roots can now be found. It is only a question of time when Ginseng, at the present rate of destruction, will be utterly exterminated from our forests. Last year more of the root was exported to China from this country by 80,000 pounds than was ever sent before in any single year, and notwithstanding the growing scarcity there are ten persons hunting for the roots now where there was one ten years ago.

O'Gorman, D. A. "Ginseng and its Cultivation in Corea." *The Journal of the Manchester Geographical Society*. Vol. 9 (1893), pp. 262–263. [O'Gorman's note is less informative on Korea than it is on ginseng's use among the American Indians, for which it is one of the few sources, though perhaps not an entirely trustworthy one.]

Some aboriginal tribes in this country [U.S.A.] have the highest respect for ginseng, regarding it as a very powerful medicine. In the mountains of western North Carolina the Cherokees gather it. These Indians call the ginseng the "Very Great Man," and, when they find a specimen, they repeat a formula taught to them by their priests, saying:

"O Mountain, I have come to take a piece from your side."

Then the finder picks up the plant and puts a glass bead in the hole to pay the mountain for it. The seventh plant found has special medicinal value, and the first four plants discovered must not be touched, though after others have been gathered the searcher may go back and collect these four.

Groot, J. J. M. de. "The Soul in Philosophy and Folk-conception: On Ginseng." *The Religious System of China*. Vol. 4, book 2, part 1. Leiden, 1897, pp. 314–317.

By far the most renowned of all medicinal roots is that which Europeans know as ginseng, as the *Shwoh wen* vocabulary defines it, "a medicinal herb produced in Shang-tang," in southeast Shansi, and in the *Ts'ien fu lun* there is the following passage, "To cure disease, we must have jen-sen". . . In none of the Classics is the drug mentioned, and we know no book of pre-Christian times in which its name occurs.

The fact that ginseng is often called in medical works *t'u-tsing* or *ti tsing,* "tsing or vital energy of the soil" testifies decisively that . . . it owes its supposed curative virtue to an animation borrowed from the earth. The first of those names occurs already in the *I yuen,* thus being at least as old as the fifth century. Another reason for the plant being believed to be animated, is its possessing a forked root, which reminds one of human forms. Li Shi-chen [compiler of a 52-volume encyclopedic work on medicine, the *Pen-ts'ao kang mu,* published in 1596] says, "that whereas its root resembles a man in shape and thus possesses a shen, it is called jen-sen," that is to say, man-sen. So, like man, the plant has a dual soul, the one borrowed from the earth, and the other, as all shen are, from heaven. More than a thousand years before Li Shi-chen lived, the author of the *I yuen* wrote,

"Jen-sen is named also tsing of the soil. The Shang-tang kind is the best, as the human shape it possesses there is complete in every respect. It wails there like a child. In bygone times, some people digging for the plant had just thrust their hoes into the ground, when they heard a plaintive wailing inside it. They dug on the spot where the sound came from, and found in fact ginseng." It is even recorded in the standard history of the Sui dynasty, "that in Kao Tsu's reign [589–605] there was in Shang-tang a house, behind which every night a man was heard calling. The inmates sought for him, but they found nobody. They discovered, however, at one mile from the house, a ginseng root with big twigs and luxuriant foliage, which they unearthed, to find that the root was more than five feet long, and shaped in every respect like a man. On this the cries were heard no more."

It is further written [in the *Pen-ts'ao kang mu*] that ginseng "strengthens the five viscera, sets at rest the vital shen, puts an end to timorousness, removes noxious influences, and sharpens the eyesight, opening the heart, and increasing knowledge and wisdom. And if consumed for some length of time, it renders the body light and prolongs life." . . . As may be expected, the root is especially recommended for diseases caused by separation of the hwun [soul] from the body, as when the soul, having passed out of the body during sleep, cannot return into it on account of one or more viscera having been in the meantime occupied by obnoxious influences.

Bishop, Isabella Bird. *Korea and her Neighbors.* New York, 1898, pp. 296–297.

[Mrs. Bishop was an Englishwoman, a tireless traveler and prolific writer. On her trip to Korea she was one of the first Westerners to visit the ginseng fields and factories.]

Everything about the factories is scrupulously clean, and would do credit to European management . . . There are two officials sent from Seoul by the Agricultural Department for the "season," with four policemen and two attendants, whose expenses are paid by the manufacturers, and each step of the manufacture and the egress of the workmen are carefully watched . . .

Ginseng is steamed for twenty-four hours in large earthen jars over iron pots built into furnaces, and is then partially dried in a room kept at a high temperature by charcoal. The final drying is effected by exposing the roots in elevated flat baskets to the rays of the bright winter sun. The human resemblance survives these processes, but afterwards the "beards" and "tails," used chiefly in Korea, are cut off, and the trunk, from three to four inches long, looks like a piece of clouded amber. These trunks are carefully picked over, and being classified according to size, are neatly packed in small oblong boxes containing about five catties [1 catty = 1.3 pounds, avoirdupois] each, twelve or fourteen of these being packed in a basket, which is waterproofed and matted, and stamped and sealed by the Agricultural Department as ready for exportation. A basket, according to quality, is worth from $14,000 to $20,000! In a good season the grower makes about fifteen times his outlay.

Nash, George V. *American Ginseng: its Commercial History, Protection and Cultivation.* U.S. Department of Agriculture, Division of Botany, Bulletin no. 16. (Rev. ed., M. G. Kains.) Washington, 1898, p. 7.

[The U.S. Government produced several bulletins on growing ginseng and fighting the diseases brought on by widespread cultivation. This one includes the best account of the early, abortive Canadian ginseng trade.]

The Indies Company permitted its officers to trade personally in ginseng with the Chinese until 1751, when they withdrew the privilege and assumed the trade themselves. Ginseng was at this time worth about 12 francs per pound in Canada, but the Company soon paid 33 francs for it. The trade continued to advance until 1752 when, in the effort to meet an excessive demand from France, a poor lot of root was placed on the market. The merchants at Rochelle directed their agents at Quebec to purchase ginseng at any price. The agents accordingly caused a large amount to be collected out of season, and this was improperly dried in ovens. Even the poor material thus obtained brought about 25 francs per pound in Quebec, and a quantity was shipped to Rochelle, amounting in value to 500,000 francs. A part of this was sent to China, where the people refused to use it. The Canadian root thus acquired a bad reputation among the Chinese, so that by 1754 the trade was reduced to a value of 30,000 francs, and soon afterwards entirely ceased.

Griffis, William Elliot. *Corea, the Hermit Nation.* 7th ed. New York, 1904, pp. 388–389.

America became a commercial rival to Cho-sen [Korea] as early as 1757, when the products of Connecticut and Massachusetts lay side by side with Corean imports in the markets of Peking and Canton. Ginseng, the most precious drug in the Chinese pharmacopœia, had been for ages brought from Manchuria and the neighboring peninsula . . .

When it was found in America the Dutch, shipping the bundled root on their galliots down the Hudson, and thence to Amsterdam and London, sold them to the British East India Company at a profit of five hundred per cent. Landed at Canton, and thence carried to Peking, American ginseng broke the market, forced the price to a shockingly low figure, and dealt a heavy blow to the Corean monopoly.

Henceforth a steady stream of ginseng—found in limitless quantities in the Ohio and Mississippi valleys—poured into

China. Though far inferior to the best article, it is sufficiently like it in taste and real or imaginary qualities to rival the root of Cho-sen, which is not of the very highest grade . . .

The war for independence over, Captain John Greene, in the ship Empress of China, sailed from New York, February 22, 1784 [with a cargo of ginseng]. Major Samuel Shaw, the supercargo, without government aid or recognition, established American trade with China, living at Canton during part of the year 1786 and the whole of 1787 and 1788, [and was] appointed consul by President Washington in 1789.

Arseniev, V. K. "Les chercheurs de ginseng dans le territoire de l'Oussouri." (H. Nicolet de Cholet, trans.) *Bulletin de l'Université l'Aurore* (Shanghai). Ser. 3, vol. 3, no. 1 (1935), pp. 320–329.

[Arseniev made many expeditions to the Far East, and this extract, concerning a strange by-product of ginseng therapy, is from a work on the Chinese in the Ussuri, published in Khabarovsk in 1914.]

Not so very long ago, it was the custom that when a rich Chinese was at the point of death, he would be given a fairly strong dose of ginseng of good quality, such as that from the province of Kirin, with the aim of prolonging his life as long as possible, so that he could express some last wishes, or perhaps take leave of one of the members of his family who, living far from the ancestral home, had not had the time to come and bid farewell to his dying relative.

When the dying man had passed away, his body as a rule was put into a coffin. Then the ginseng vapors would arise from the corpse and begin to condense on the interior of the coffin lid. After many years there would be formed a protuberance, looking like a mushroom, and called "dead man's mushroom."

They say it has a dark-colored solid body, which recalls the anthropomorphic shape of ginseng; it is one of the world's most precious medicines, especially for the cure of consumptives. It is claimed that the search for this mushroom is not an easy thing, that many dangers await the daring man who tries to open tombs, even abandoned ones. The noxious vapors which arise from coffins are very dangerous, especially when the mushroom is still being formed.

There are evidently numerous imitations and numberless frauds. One day, while walking in a Chinese city, I saw a Chinese worker who had furnished himself with all the tools necessary for breaking into tombs, who was selling, or so he said, a dead man's mushroom. With great volubility he told the passers-by that, as a mason, he had had the unexpected luck to discover, somewhere "in the interior," the abandoned tomb of a rich Chinese who died during the Ming dynasty. Pleased by this windfall, he worked for a long time to open the tomb, and found adhering to the inner lid and just in front of the skeleton's mouth, a magnificent dead man's mushroom, which he offered for cash to the many curious who had gathered around him.

To prove what he was saying, and so that no one could doubt the miraculous virtues of this rarest of mushrooms, he dropped a tiny piece in a small glass of wine. The wine immediately changed from white into a beautiful red color.

Bowman, N. H. (M.D.) "The History of Korean Medicine." *Transactions of the Korean Branch of the Royal Asiatic Society*. Vol. 6 (1915), p. 9.

Twenty years after the Pon-cho [the "first manuscript," an ancient—3rd millennium B.C.—compilation of Korean medical information] received imperial sanction by the Emperor Sin-chong [about A.D. 1628], the famous Chinese and Korean market called Moon-chang ["Door of trade"] was established in N.E. China in the Leaotung or Yotong province 700 li (233 English miles) from the nearest Korean prefecture, Wiju, and 300 li (100 English miles) from the Eastern border of the Leaotung province which was the Yalu River, the N.W. boundary of Korea. The market was established at the close of the Ming dynasty [ended in 1644], . . . and was continued for a period of 230 years, during which time it was the greatest ginseng market in the world. The market . . . was the only point in Chinese territory at that time open to Korean merchantmen. The Koreans took their merchandise there for sale and the Chinese did likewise. The trade consisted chiefly of ginseng from Korea and silk from China; however there were other commodities bought and sold by both countrymen. The Pon-cho became the official catalogue of classification for all medicines of the two countries and any not contained in the Pon-cho were marked under some disadvantage.

Sowerby, Arthur de Carle. *The Naturalist in Manchuria*. Vol. 1: *Travel and Exploration*. Tientsin, 1922, p. 296.

[Sowerby was one of the first explorers to visit the native tribes of Manchuria. He was primarily a botanist, however, and his report contains nothing about these peoples' relationship to ginseng.]

The men [of the "Fish-skin Tartars"] wore Chinese and semi-foreign dress, especially in regard to headgear. They all owned huge coats of roe-deer skin, with high collars and caps with turn-down flaps to match. The hair of the animal was outside. One or two who were in hunting dress had the peculiar smoked-leather moccasins known in Manchuria as *wula*. These are used by all who go into the forest, and most of the farmers and settlers in the forest regions. They are generally worn much too large, and the foot is bound round with what is known as *wula ts'ao* or wula grass, a peculiarly fine, soft and springy grass with long fibres. The latter is twisted right up the leg, and the thongs or ropes, that keep the moccasins on are wound right up the leg . . . to keep the feet warm and dry. The Manchurians look upon the *wula* grass as of great value, for without it none could survive frostbite in the feet in winter. The Chinese have a couplet which runs:

Kuan-tung ch'eng san teng hao
Jen-seng tiao-pi wula ts'ao

which may be rendered in English:

Three valuable things hail from east of the pass
Ginseng, sable-skin and *wula* grass

Kuan-tung means "east of the pass," and is the Chinese name for Manchuria, as that country lies east of the pass at Shan-hai kuan.

Crane, Louise. "The Manchurian Man-Image." *Asia.* Vol. 29 (1929), pp. 202–207.
[This article contains four rare photographs of ginseng cultivation and processing in Manchuria.]

Lattimore, Owen. "The Gold Tribe, 'Fishskin Tatars' of the Lower Sungari." *Memoirs of the American Anthropological Association,* 1933. Reprinted in *Studies in Frontier History.* London, 1962, pp. 368–369.

[Lattimore is an extremely acute observer of tribal life in Manchuria and Mongolia. Many of the comments here confirm earlier observations, though the ginseng plant would not be in flower as late as August.]

Another summer "hunt" is that for ginseng. It is also a "hot" medicine, more powerful and of more general use than "bloodhorn." It has the sovereign place in the old Chinese pharmacopeia, ranking as the best of all tonics—one able to resuscitate those on the point of death and prolonging life when all other means fail. Ginseng buyers are connoisseurs; the value of the plant varies enormously according to shape, the number of tendrils or roots, their pattern, and so forth. Wild ginseng is worth much more than cultivated, and Manchurian ginseng is considered the best of all; especially that growing on the Ch'ang-pai-shan, the holy range of the Manchu. It is credited with quasi-human qualities (as indeed its Chinese name, *jen-shen,* implies) and said to live, as it were, in families or tribes. When a whole family of ginseng is found, with its patriarchal "ancestor," the latter has a fabulous value. Whether ginseng was quite as much esteemed in China before the time of the Manchu, I do not know. It was an article of tribute at least as early as the T'ang dynasty. Certainly under the Manchu it enjoyed a special kind of imperial favor, and its collection and distribution

Index